American Language Hub

LEVEL 1
Workbook with Key

+ access to **Audio**

ADRIAN TENNANT

Macmillan Education
4 Crinan Street
London N1 9XW
A division of Macmillan Education Limited

Companies and representatives throughout the world

American Language Hub Level 1 Workbook with Key ISBN 978-1-786-32404-7
American Language Hub Level 1 Workbook with Key + access to Audio
ISBN 978-1-786-32401-6

Text, design and illustration © Macmillan Education Limited 2020
Written by Adrian Tennant

The author has asserted their right to be identified as the author of this work
in accordance with the Copyright, Designs and Patents Act 1988.

First published 2020

All rights reserved. No part of this publication may be reproduced, stored
in a retrieval system, or transmitted in any form or by any means, electronic,
mechanical, photocopying, recording, or otherwise, without the prior written
permission of the publishers.

Designed by SPi-Global
Cover design based on original design by Restless
Cover illustration/photograph by Plainpicture/Cultura/dotdotred
Picture research by Emily Taylor

The authors and publishers would like to thank the following for permission
to reproduce their photographs:

Alamy/Art Directors p6(9), Alamy/Magone p46(1), Alamy/Mode Images p6(6),
Alamy/Robert Mora p6(5), Alamy/Tom Viggars p6(7); **BananaStock** p22(5);
Digital Vision p40(3); **Ehaurylik** p50(3); **Getty Images** pp40(2), 46(2,9), 48(cl),
52(1), 66(7, 11), 68, 74, Getty Images/Emad Aljumah p33(3), Getty Images/
Allsport Concepts Creative p66(4), Getty Images/Carlo Amoruso p4(cr), Getty
Images/Andrea Zanchi Photography p49, Getty Images/Petek Arici p42(4),
Getty Images/Thomas Barwick pp22(3), 43(1), 56, 68(1), Getty Images/Blend
Images pp13, 16, 35, 55, 66(3), 68(3), Getty Images/Alistair Berg p52(4), Getty
Images/Nick Brundle p58(cl), Getty Images/Anna Bryukhanova p42(2), Getty
Images/Paul Burns p29(3), Getty Images/Peter Cade p24(br), Getty Images/
Caiaimage pp15, 61(bl), Getty Images/Caiaimage/Martin Barraud p28(2),
Getty Images/Nano Calvo p22(7), Getty Images/Cheryl Chan p18, Getty
Images/Petar Chernaev p42(3), Getty Images/Paolo Cipriani p42(5), Getty
Images/Claudiodivizia p30(tr), Getty Images/George Clerk p28(4), Getty
Images/CoffeeAndMilk p11(1), Getty Images/Corbis p52(3), Getty Images/
Cultura pp22(6), 25(3), 26, 27, 47, 50(2), 53(tl), 67, 69(br), 70, Getty Images/
Robert Decelis p57, Getty Images/Digital Vision pp43(3), 52(2), 68(5,6), Getty
Images/Pablo Blazquez Dominguez p39, Getty Images/Dorling Kindersley
pp28(5), 66(9), Getty Images/Richard Drury pp22(2), 25(1), Getty Images/
E+ pp7(br), 52(a), 68(tr,tl), Getty Images/Wayne Eastep p29(5), Getty Images/
EyeEm pp7(tr), 46(4), 52(b,c,d), 58(tl), 61(tl), 62(1), 75, Getty Images/FatCamera
p22(4), Getty Images/fstop123 p28(8), Getty Images/Gerenme p28(7),
Getty Images/Hero Images pp10, 21, 22(8), 69(tcr), Getty Images/Hoxton
p22(1), Getty Images/Imagemore p66(2), Getty Images/Images Bazaar
p14, Getty Images/iStockphoto pp17, 23, 34(5,6), 51, 74(b), Getty Images/
JazzIRT p28(9), Getty Images/Jeff Kauck Photography p48(tr), Getty Images/
Roos Koole p69(bcr), Getty Images/Jenifoto p29(4), Getty Images/Johner RF
p68(4), Getty Images/Fabio Lamanna p25(2), Getty Images/Loop Images/
Alan Novelli p54, Getty Images/Maremagnum p32, Getty Images/Maskot
p7(tcr), Getty Images/Mbbirdy p29(2), Getty Images/Nicolas McComber
p8, Getty Images/Mint Images p34(2), Getty Images/Moment p64, Getty
Images/National Geographic Creative p66(6), Getty Images/Thomas Northcut
p53(bl), Getty Images/Pagadesign p74(c), Getty Images/Passage pp60(b), 65,
Getty Images/PeopleImages p66(5), Getty Images/PhotoDisc p6(8), Getty
Images/Photolibrary p46(3), Getty Images/PhotoAlto/Odilon Dimier p37,
Getty Images/Tanatat Pongpibool p59, Getty Images/Martin Poole p46(5),
Getty Images/Andre Schoenherr p62(2), Getty Images/Oleh Slobodeniuk
p4(br), Getty Images/Alexander Spatari p41, Getty Images/Chad Springer
p20, Getty Images/Shannon Stent p66(8), Getty Images/Stockbyte p11(6),
Getty Images/Stone Sub p7(bcr), Getty Images/Paul Strowger p11(2), Getty
Images/Punnawit Suwuttananun p33(2), Getty Images/Svetikd p4(tr), Getty
Images/The Image Bank pp11(3,5), 43(2), 71, 72, Getty Images/Tbradford p45,
Getty Images/Topic Images p28(3), Getty Images/Betsie Van der Meer p42(1),
Getty Images/Guy Vanderelst p30(cr), Getty Images/Klaus Vedfelt p34(1),
Getty Images/Venusphoto p28(6), Getty Images/VisitBritain p34(4), Getty
Images/VisitBritain/Britain on View p29(6), Getty Images/Sharon Vos-Arnold
p40(1), Getty Images/WendellandCarolyn p6(3), Getty Images/Westend61,
p33(1), 60(tl), 66(10,12), 73, Getty Images/Simon Winnall p38, Getty Images/
Natalie Winter p58(bl), Getty Images/Yagi Studio p63, Getty Images/Bahadir
Yeniceri p46(7); **Dave G Kelly** p66(1); **Tara Moore** p11(4); **Photodisc**/C
Squared Studios p40(6); **Scanrail** p6(10); **Shutterstock**/Dokmaihaeng p50(1),
Shutterstock/Mega_Pixel p6(12), Shutterstock/MJTH p24(tl), Shutterstock/
Pix11 p28(10), Shutterstock/Rawpixel.com p29(1), Shutterstock/S-F p40(5),

Shutterstock/Alexander Tolstykh p28(1), Shutterstock/Vladi333 p19;
Springer Nature Limited p46(10); **Stockbyte** p6(2), Stockbyte/John Foxx
p40(4); **Thinkstock** pp6(1,4, 11), 34(3), 46(8); **Up the Resolution** p46(6).

These materials may contain links for third party websites. We have no control
over, and are not responsible for, the contents of such third party websites.
Please use care when accessing them.

The inclusion of any specific companies, commercial products, trade names or
otherwise does not constitute or imply its endorsement or recommendation
by Macmillan Education Limited.

Printed and bound in Mexico
by Compañía Editorial Ultra, S.A. de C.V.

2021   2020
6   5   4   3

Contents

U1	ARRIVALS
(p4–9)	**G** simple present *be*: positive and negative; simple present *be*: questions; *a/an* and plural nouns; *this, that, these, those*
	V countries and nationalities; big numbers; everyday items
	P syllable stress; similar numbers; vowel sounds: /ɪ/ /æ/ /iː/ /oʊ/
	W fill in a form with personal details

U2	PEOPLE
(p10–15)	**G** possessive adjectives and apostrophes; *have/has*; using adjectives
	V family; describing appearance; personality adjectives
	P /ə/ 'schwa'; *have/has*; syllable stress: adjectives
	W write an email to a friend

U3	DAYS
(p16–21)	**G** simple present positive; adverbs of frequency; simple present negative
	V everyday activities; prepositions of time; big celebrations
	P third person -s; word stress; sentence stress
	W write a blog post about your day

U4	WORK AND EDUCATION
(p22–27)	**G** simple present *yes/no* questions; short answers; *have to / don't have to*; question words
	V work and jobs; time expressions; education collocations
	P linking sounds: *do/does*; connected speech: *have to*; word stress: questions
	W write an email asking for information

U5	PLACES
(p28–33)	**G** *there is / are*; *can*; imperatives
	V rooms and furniture; prepositions of place; places in a town or city; adjectives to describe the appearance of things
	P /b/, /d/ and /g/; weak forms: *can/can't*; word stress: adjectives
	W write a description of a place

U6	THAT'S ENTERTAINMENT
(p34–39)	**G** likes and dislikes; *was/were*; simple past regular and irregular verbs
	V entertainment; past time expressions; life events
	P word stress: noun patterns; weak forms: *was/were*; simple past regular endings
	W write a review of an event

U7	TRAVEL AND TRANSPORTATION
(p40–45)	**G** *could*; simple past negative; simple past questions
	V transportation; travel phrases; verb phrases
	P /eɪ/ and /oʊ/; word stress: cities; connected speech
	W write a short article about a travel experience

U8	FOOD AND DRINK
(p46–51)	**G** countable and uncountable nouns; *some* and *any*; *much, many, a lot of*; *a/an, the,* no article
	V food and drink; containers; food preparation
	P plurals; short and long vowel sounds; consonant clusters
	W write an online restaurant review

U9	SHOPPING
(p52–57)	**G** present progressive; simple present vs present progressive; object pronouns
	V clothes; present time expressions; stores and services
	P /ɜː/; /ŋ/; /tʃ/ and /ʃ/
	W write a social media post

U10	THE GREAT OUTDOORS
(p58–63)	**G** comparatives; superlatives; verb + *to* + infinitive
	V landscape features; seasons and weather; phrasal verbs
	P weak forms: /ə/ in *than*; /oʊ/ and /aʊ/; weak forms: /tuː/ and /tə/
	W write a product review

U11	THE BODY
(p64–69)	**G** *should* and *shouldn't*; present perfect; present perfect vs simple past
	V the body; irregular past participles; sports
	P sentence stress; past participles; contractions
	W write a recommendation on a forum

U12	MODERN LIVES
(p70–75)	**G** *going to*; *will* for predictions; *might*
	V future time expressions; collocations with *get*; internet communication
	P *going to*: weak and strong *to*; contractions: *'ll*; diphthongs
	W write a formal email

AUDIO SCRIPTS	
(p76–80)	

ANSWER KEY	
(p81–96)	

1.1 Arrivals — People and places

VOCABULARY
Countries and nationalities

A Match countries (1–10) with the words in the box.

| Brazil | Canada | China | France | India |
| Japan | Mexico | Spain | Turkey | US |

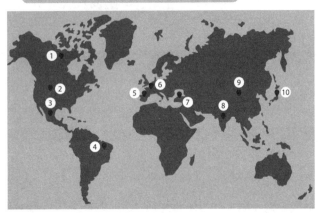

B Choose the correct options to complete the conversations.

a
Megan: Hi, I'm Megan. I'm from Vancouver in ¹*Canada / Canadian*. I'm ²*Canada / Canadian*.
Keiko: I'm Keiko. I'm ³*Japan / Japanese*, but I live in ⁴*Mexico / Mexican*. This is my husband, Carlos. He's ⁵*Mexico / Mexican*.

b
Interviewer: Jin Li? That's an interesting name. Are you ⁶*China / Chinese*?
Jin Li: Ha ha! Well, my father is from ⁷*China / Chinese*, but my mother is ⁸*Britain / British*.

c
Lars: Hello. I'm Lars. I work for ZHEP Technology in Stockholm, ⁹*Sweden / Swedish*.
Andreas: Oh, my wife is ¹⁰*Sweden / Swedish*; we go there every year! I'm Andreas, by the way.

PRONUNCIATION
Syllable stress

🔊 Complete the table with the words in the box. Then listen, 1.1 check and repeat.

| Brazil | British | Canadian | Colombia | ~~Indian~~ |
| Japan | Japanese | Mexican | Polish | Vietnam |

●●	●●	●●●	●●●	●●●●
		Indian		

GRAMMAR
Simple present *be*: positive and negative

A Complete the sentences with the correct form of *be*.

| aren't | 'm | 'm not | is | isn't | 're |

1 Hi! I _____ your new teacher, Mr. Foley.
2 I'm Lucy and this is my sister Mia. We _____ from Sydney, Australia.
3 That's Dev. He _____ from New York.
4 Ha ha! I _____ from Japan, I'm from China.
5 No, my parents _____ French. They're from Belgium.
6 No, she _____. She's Vietnamese.

B Complete introductions (a–c) with the correct form of *be*. Use contractions where possible.

a Hi, I ¹_____ Emily and this ²_____ my boyfriend, Noah. I ³_____ Canadian, but Noah ⁴_____. He ⁵_____ from the US. In the picture we ⁶_____ on a skiing vacation in Corvara, Italy.

b This ⁷_____ a picture of my sister Amy. We ⁸_____ American, but our parents ⁹_____. They ¹⁰_____ Chinese, but they live in the US. Amy has a boyfriend named Minh. He ¹¹_____ Vietnamese.

c Hi, I ¹²_____ Elsa and this is a picture of me on vacation. I live in London, but I ¹³_____ British, I ¹⁴_____ from Sweden. I live in an apartment with two friends, Camille and Alicia. They ¹⁵_____ both French.

4 ARRIVALS

1.2 Arrivals — Where are you?

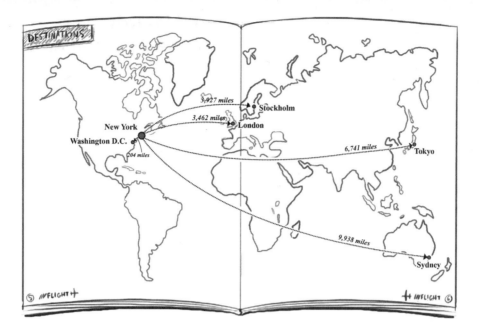

VOCABULARY
Big numbers

A Write the numbers.

1. Nine hundred and thirty-seven.　　937
2. Twenty-five thousand, three hundred and twelve.　　_____
3. Nine thousand, seven hundred and thirty.　　_____
4. Two and a half million.　　_____
5. Eighteen thousand, eight hundred and eighty.　　_____
6. Three hundred and sixteen.　　_____

B Look at the flight map. Match distances (1–5) with flight paths (a–e).

1. Nine thousand, nine hundred and thirty-eight miles.
2. Three thousand, four hundred and sixty-two miles.
3. Two hundred and four miles.
4. Six thousand, seven hundred and forty-one miles.
5. Three thousand, nine hundred and twenty-seven miles.

a. New York to Tokyo.
b. New York to London.
c. New York to Stockholm.
d. New York to Washington D.C.
e. New York to Sydney.

PRONUNCIATION
Similar numbers

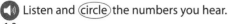 Listen and (circle) the numbers you hear.

1. My sister's name is Emily. She's *13 / 30* years old.
2. The flight from New York to Tokyo is *14 / 40* hours long.
3. It's my father's birthday today. He's *16 / 60* years old.
4. It's really sunny outside, but only about *15 / 50* degrees.
5. In some countries, *13 / 30* is a lucky number.
6. Tickets cost $*18 / 80* each.

GRAMMAR
Simple present *be*: questions

A Correct the mistakes in each question.

1. Where *are* you ~~are~~ from?
2. Tell me about the city. It is expensive?
3. Is your parents Japanese?
4. Hi, Erin! How you are?
5. It is hot there?
6. What your favorite type of food?
7. Oh, really? Where you are now?
8. You is busy?

B Reorder the words to make questions with *be*.

1
James: _____Where are you from?_____
(from / where / you / are / ?)
Soo-Jin: I'm from Seoul in South Korea.

2
Sean: _____
(Spanish / you / are / ?)
María: No, I'm not. I'm from Guadalajara in Mexico.

3
Gemma: _____
(Seoul / Paris / far / is / from / how / ?)
Flight attendant: Seoul is 5,568 miles from Paris.

4
Alicia: _____
(you / where / now / are / ?)
Antoine: I'm at the airport.

5
Alex: _____
(favorite / your / food / what's / ?)
Patrick: My favorite food is Indian food. I love it!

ARRIVALS　5

1.3 Arrivals — What's in your bag?

VOCABULARY
Everyday items
Label pictures (1–12) with the words in the box.

> bottle of water   credit card   headphones   keys
> laptop   magazine   cell phone   money   tissues
> umbrella   wallet   watch

1 _____

2 _____

3 _____

4 _____

5 _____

6 _____

7 _____   8 _____

9 _____   10 _____

11 _____   12 _____

GRAMMAR
a/an and plural nouns; *this, that, these, those*

A Complete the sentences with *a*, *an* or – (no article).

1 Heathrow is _____ airport in London.
2 Take _____ umbrella – it's raining!
3 Tonya is _____ French student.
4 There's _____ money in my backpack.
5 Send me _____ email when you arrive.
6 Mexico is _____ country in North America.
7 He travels to a lot of _____ countries for work.
8 Harvard is _____ university in the US.

B Complete conversations (a–c) with *this, that, these* or *those*.

a
João: Hey, is ¹*this / that* your sister over there?
Sam: Yes, it is.
João: Who are ²*these / those* people with her?
Sam: I think they're her friends from work.

b
Mr. Clarke: Lucas, is ³*this / those* your bag?
Lucas: Yes, it is. Sorry, sir.
Mr. Clarke: Hmm … and are ⁴*that / these* your books?
Lucas: Uh … yes, sir.

c
Airport security: Excuse me! Are ⁵*these / those* your watches here?
Passenger: Yes, they are. But ⁶*this / that* one there isn't mine.
Airport security: I see … and why do you have six watches?
Passenger: I collect watches. It's my hobby.

PRONUNCIATION
Vowel sounds: /ɪ/ /æ/ /iː/ /oʊ/

🔊 Listen and (circle) the word in each group that has a different vowel sound.
1.3

1	(key)	this	big
2	close	phone	book
3	wallet	bag	that
4	key	it	see
5	watch	that	bag
6	toes	those	tissues

6   ARRIVALS

1.4 Arrivals   Reading

Boarding Pass

Different people, different luggage
SARAH M | 10:17 am

People travel for lots of different reasons. Some travel for fun, others travel for business. But everyone takes something different with them on the plane. Today, I'm at Heathrow Airport to ask people one simple question – What's in your bag and why?

Greg: What's in my bag? Well I'm going skiing in Italy, so I have a sweater for when it's cold. I also have a map, some water and sunglasses. I need to take everything with me, as I don't have lots of money. It's important my bag is easy to carry and isn't heavy. Oh, and I also have some headphones to listen to music on my phone.

Elsa: I travel a lot for work so I have a few very important things in my carry-on bag. I have a laptop, my cell phone and a credit card from work to pay for everything. I also have a magazine because I like to read on the plane when I don't have any work to do.

Ralph: Well, it's difficult as I have to carry things for Harry, here. So I have tissues and other things for a baby. There's not a lot of space for my things, but I do have a cell phone and a newspaper to read when he goes to sleep.

Sandra: What do I have in my bag? I don't really know. The usual things like my phone, money, a bottle of water. I always take a big bag so I can take everything I might need. Let's see … yes, I have an umbrella, some keys and a sandwich. Yes, it's important to have food.

READING

A READ FOR GIST Read *Boarding Pass: Different people, different luggage* and complete the summaries with Greg, Elsa, Ralph or Sandra.

1 _____'s carry-on bag has important things for business in it.
2 _____ has a big bag with money, water and food in it.
3 A lot of things in _____'s bag are for a baby.
4 _____ has everything he needs for a vacation in Italy.

Glossary
space (n) an empty or available area

B READ FOR DETAIL Read the article again. Complete the sentences with no more than two words from the article.

1 Greg has a sweater for when it gets _____ on vacation.
2 He also has some _____ to listen to music.
3 Elsa uses her _____ from work to pay for everything.
4 When she doesn't have any _____ to do on the plane, Elsa reads a magazine.
5 Most of the things in Ralph's bag are for his _____, Harry.
6 When Harry goes to sleep, Ralph reads _____.
7 Sandra has a big bag so she can carry _____ she needs.
8 She thinks it's important to _____ in her bag.

C REFLECT Answer the questions.

1 What's in your bag today?
2 What do you take with you on vacation?
3 What do you take to work/school?

1.5 Arrivals — Listening; Functional Language

LISTENING

A LISTEN FOR GIST Listen to a conversation about Vietnam and answer the questions.

1 Who does Max talk to?
   a His mom   b His dad   c His sister
2 Where is Max?
   a At a golf club   b On vacation   c At work
3 Why does Max need his coat?
   a Because it's cold
   b Because it's snowing
   c Because it's raining
4 Which topic doesn't Max talk about?
   a The food   b The weather   c The stores

Glossary
grasshopper (n) a large green insect that jumps around on its long back legs
strange (adj) surprising or unusual

B LISTEN FOR DETAIL Listen again. Are the sentences true (T) or false (F)? Correct the false sentences.

1 Max is in Hanoi, Vietnam.   T / F
2 It's really cold and raining a lot.   T / F
3 Max doesn't like Vietnamese food.   T / F
4 His mother doesn't want him to eat insects.   T / F
5 Max's next destination is Thailand.   T / F
6 Max says he needs more money.   T / F

C REFLECT Answer the questions.

1 Is Max's mom worried, angry or sad? How do you know?
2 Why does Max say 'Thailand, I think' when his mom asks where his next destination is?
3 Would you like to go to Vietnam? Why/Why not?

FUNCTIONAL LANGUAGE
Greeting people and making introductions

Complete the conversation with the words in the box. Then listen and check.

| fine | how | I'm | meet | this | too |

Max: Excuse me, is this the train to Sapa?
Emily: Yes, it is.
Max: Oh, great. Thanks. ¹_____ Max by the way.
Emily: Nice to ²_____ you Max. I'm Emily and ³_____ is my friend Sophie.
Max: Nice to meet you both. ⁴_____ are you?
Emily: Not ⁵_____ bad. And you?
Max: I'm ⁶_____, thanks.
Emily: So where are you from, Max?

8 ARRIVALS

1.6 Arrivals — Fill in a form with personal details

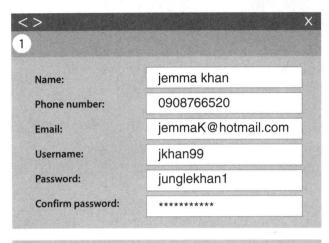

WRITING

A Match forms (1–3) with places (a–c).

a at a hotel
b on a plane
c an online account

B Complete form 3 with the words in the box.

| Duration | Email | First | Home | Number | Occupation |
| Payment | Phone | Last | Type |

C Look at forms 1 and 2. Find and correct five mistakes with capital letters.

WRITING PRACTICE

Imagine you are at a language school. Complete the registration form. Remember to use capital letters correctly.

Registration form for English classes.

First name: _____   Nationality: _____

Last name: _____   Email: _____

Date of birth: _____   Phone number: _____

Duration of course: 3 weeks ☐   6 weeks ☐   12 weeks ☐

Payment type: Cash ☐   Debit card ☐   Credit card ☐

ARRIVALS 9

2.1 People — Family

VOCABULARY
Family

Look at the family tree. Complete the sentences with the words in the box.

> aunt ~~brother~~ children cousins father
> grandfather grandmother husband
> mother parents sister uncle wife

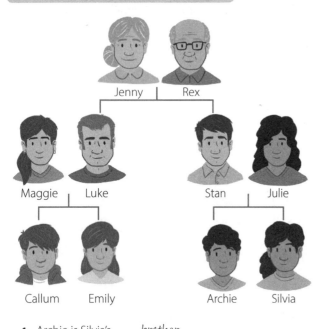

1 Archie is Silvia's ___brother___.
2 Maggie is Callum's _____.
3 Luke is Maggie's _____.
4 Jenny is Callum's _____.
5 Stan is Emily's _____.
6 Archie and Silvia are Callum's _____.
7 Rex is Emily and Silvia's _____.
8 Julie and Stan are Archie's _____.
9 Emily is Callum's _____.
10 Jenny is Rex's _____.
11 Maggie is Archie's _____.
12 Emily and Callum are Luke's _____.
13 Rex is Luke's _____.

PRONUNCIATION
/ə/ 'schwa'

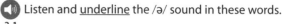 Listen and underline the /ə/ sound in these words.

1 cousin
2 famous
3 husband
4 curious
5 actress
6 celebrate
7 family
8 again

GRAMMAR
Possessive adjectives and apostrophes

A Complete the paragraph with the possessive adjectives in the box.

> her his its my our their

This is a picture of [1]_____ wife Felicity with [2]_____ friends Bea and Jenna. They come to [3]_____ house every Monday for coffee. [4]_____ children are both four months old. Bea has a son. [5]_____ name is Reuben. Jenna's daughter Evelyn has a toy dinosaur that she takes everywhere. [6]_____ name is Dino!

B Choose the correct options to complete the sentences.

1 My *parents'* / *parent's* dog is named Rufus.
2 What's your *sisters'* / *sister's* name?
3 My *wife's* / *wifes'* favorite food is sushi.
4 My *grandparent's* / *grandparents'* names are David and Sue.
5 Amazon is a great place to buy *childrens'* / *children's* books.
6 I think she's married to *Davids'* / *David's* sister.
7 What color is *James'* / *James's* bag?
8 I start my new job in two *week's* / *weeks'* time.

2.2 People — The same, but different

VOCABULARY
Describing appearance

A Match pictures (1–6) with descriptions (a–f).

1 _____   2 _____

3 _____   4 _____

5 _____   6 _____

a Alexa has **long, straight** brown hair and glasses.
b James is **bald** and has glasses and a **mustache**.
c Damian has **short** hair and a **beard**.
d Emily's hair is **curly** and **blond**.
e My grandma has short **gray** hair.
f Luke has short **brown** hair and **glasses**.

B Complete the table with the words in bold in Exercise A.

Hair length	Hair type	Hair color	Other

GRAMMAR
have/has

A Complete the sentences with the correct form of *have / has* and *does/does not*. Use contractions where possible.

1 We _____ a small house near Cambridge.
2 _____ your father have a beard?
3 Our hotel room _____ an amazing view.
4 Can you pay? I _____ any money!
5 Do you _____ a big family?
6 Karen _____ curly hair. Her hair is straight.
7 _____ Max have any children?
8 We _____ a lot of friends in the area.

B Reorder the words to make sentences and questions.

1 Ferrari / My / a / uncle / has
   _____

2 don't / and Tim / children / Amy / any / have
   _____

3 blue eyes / your / have / mother / Does / ?
   _____

4 a / He / famous / doesn't / cousin / have
   _____

5 sisters / my / Both / hair / of / have / blond
   _____

6 doesn't / sister / today / have / Danielle's / sunglasses / her
   _____

7 but / doesn't / a car / have / my / , / brother / I
   _____

8 to / have / store / We / to / time / don't / go / the
   _____

PRONUNCIATION
have/has

🔊 Listen and (circle) the correct options to complete
2.2 the sentences.

1 *He has / She has* blond hair and blue eyes.
2 *We have / They have* an office in New York.
3 *I have / They have* two sisters and one brother.
4 *He has / She has* a house in the countryside.
5 No, I think *he has / she has* an iPhone 6.
6 I hear *you have / they have* a swimming pool.
7 My boss? *She has / He has* short brown hair and glasses.
8 Yes, *we have / they have* two children – a girl and a boy.

PEOPLE 11

2.3 People — Friends

VOCABULARY
Personality adjectives

A Complete the sentences with the words in the box. Use pictures 1–5 to help you.

> friendly   messy   noisy   quiet   serious

1 My brother is really _____ – his bedroom is terrible!
2 Mike is really _____. He loves to sing and shouts a lot.
3 Silvia is always _____. She never laughs or smiles!
4 Emma is very _____. She talks to everyone and always says hello.
5 Rob doesn't like parties. He's really _____.

B Choose the correct adjectives (a, b or c) to complete the sentences.

1 Penny doesn't like talking to people. I don't know why, but she is _____.
   a funny   b messy   c unfriendly
2 I can't find my keys, because I'm so _____.
   a messy   b quiet   c sad
3 Your sister looks very _____. She's always smiling and laughing.
   a happy   b serious   c neat
4 My brother is really _____. He never stops talking and he's really loud.
   a funny   b messy   c noisy
5 Aroon's _____ because his pet goldfish died.
   a friendly   b sad   c neat
6 Why are you always so _____? You need to smile sometimes.
   a funny   b noisy   c serious
7 Please be _____! I'm trying to finish my homework.
   a happy   b noisy   c quiet

PRONUNCIATION
Syllable stress: adjectives

🔊 Complete the table with the adjectives in the box. Then
2.3 listen and check.

> blond   curly   different   neat   quiet
> serious   straight   tall   unfriendly   unhappy

●	●●	●●●	●●●

GRAMMAR
Using adjectives

A Reorder the words to make sentences and questions.

1 fairly / person / is / serious / Tristan / a
   _____

2 are / friendly / roommates / your / very
   _____

3 is / sister's / messy / my / really / bedroom
   _____

4 noisy / your / neighbors / very / are / ?
   _____

5 this / office / very / the / quiet / is / morning
   _____

6 new / expensive / is / your / apartment / ?
   _____

B Correct the mistakes in each sentence.

1 My boss isn't a very friend person. He is always shouting!
2 What happened? You're usually neat fairly.
3 Your children are both really talls.
4 My best friend is a very funny. He's always telling jokes.
5 Your parents never smile. They're serious people really.
6 Are you OK? You're quiet fairly today.

12   PEOPLE

2.4 People — Reading

Living with the De Lucas

In the US, a lot of people leave the family home when they're 18. However, this isn't true in other parts of the world. In a small village ten miles from Mexico City, three generations of the De Luca family live together. Matt Wallace finds out how they feel about living in the same house.

Mona De Luca is 24 and lives with her younger brother and sister, parents and grandparents in a small four-bedroom house. She loves her family, but finds it difficult to live in a house full of people and wants to move out to share an apartment with her friends.

'1_____,'

Ralph De Luca is Mona's father. He is the opposite of his daughter. He loves living with so many people. 'It's great.

2_____,'

His children say he is serious and he never laughs or smiles. 'It's not true.

3_____,'

Ralph's mother Sophia De Luca is 79, but with her pretty smile and brown eyes, she looks about 60.

'4_____,'

'It's normal for families to live together like this. It can be difficult sometimes, but I'm a happy person and that helps.' Talking about her family, Sophia says,

'5_____.'

They are very noisy.'

READING

A READ FOR GIST Read *Living with the De Lucas*. What is it about?

1 A big family that lives in the same house.
2 A small family that lives in a big house.
3 Different families that live in the same house.

Glossary
generation (n) a group of people, or members of a family, who are about the same age

B READ FOR DETAIL Read the article again. Are the sentences true (T) or false (F)? Correct the false sentences.

1 Mona De Luca lives with two younger brothers.   T / F
2 She wants to live with her friends, not her family.   T / F
3 Mona's grandfather is named Ralph.   T / F
4 Ralph's children think he's a very happy person.   T / F
5 Mona's grandmother is 60 years old.   T / F
6 Sophia De Luca says she is a happy person.   T / F

C READ FOR ORGANIZATION Match blanks (1–5) with sentences (a–e) to complete the article.

a I come home from work, there's always food on the table and the house is really neat.
b I love my grandchildren, but living with them is difficult.
c I love to laugh, but when I get home from work, I am tired.
d I'm too old to live at home, I need my own space.
e When people ask how old I am, they are always surprised.

D REFLECT Answer the questions.

1 Who do you share a house or apartment with?
2 Would you like to live on your own? Why/Why not?
3 What's good about living with your parents and grandparents?

2.5 People
Listening; Functional Language

LISTENING

A **LISTEN FOR KEY WORDS** Listen to a conversation about a wedding. Check (✓) the people Maha talks about.

☐ her sister ☐ her parents
☐ her brother ☐ her uncle
☐ her grandparents ☐ her brother's wife
☐ her cousin ☐ her aunt

B **LISTEN FOR DETAIL** Listen again. Match people (1–5) to descriptions (a–e).

1 Hamad   a has blue eyes and is American.
2 Fauzia   b has a beard and a mustache.
3 Maha's mother c looks serious, but is funny.
4 Maha's father d has short gray hair and wears glasses.
5 Mandy   e is slim and has long black hair.

C **REFLECT** Answer the questions.
1 How would you describe the different people in your family?
2 Do you like big family weddings? Why/Why not?

FUNCTIONAL LANGUAGE
Making and responding to requests

Complete the conversation with the words in the box. Then listen and check.

| ~~can~~ | could | course | dollars | not |
| please | problem | sorry | that | |

Doug: ¹_____Can_____ I help you?
Maha: Yes, ²_____. Could I have a coffee with milk and a green tea?
Doug: Of ³_____. Anything to eat?
Maha: ⁴_____ I have a chocolate cookie?
Doug: No, ⁵_____. I'm afraid ⁶_____. We don't have any left.
Maha: OK, no ⁷_____. How much is ⁸_____?
Doug: That's 4 ⁹_____ and 60 cents.
Maha: Thanks.

2.6 People — Write an email to a friend

WRITING

A Read the email and check (✓) the topics the person asks about.

To: e.parks@netserve.com
Sent: Wednesday February 14, 2018, 10:14 am
From: jjcampbell@freeserve.net
Subject: How's things?

Hi Emma,

How are you? Are you enjoying college? What do you study? I can't remember. Who's in your class? I know you live in an apartment near the university. Who do you live with? What are your roommates like?

Looking forward to hearing from you soon.

Best wishes,
Jenny

☐ family   ☐ who they live with
☐ friends   ☐ what they study
☐ where they live   ☐ who is in their class

B Read Emma's reply. Are the sentences true (T) or false (F)? Correct the false sentences.

To: jjcampbell@freeserve.net
Sent: Saturday February 17, 2018, 6:10 pm
From: e.parks@netserve.com
Subject: re: How's things?

Hi Jenny,

I'm very well, thanks. I'm having a great time at college [1]_____ I'm making lots of new friends.

I'm studying science. It's very difficult, [2]_____ I'm enjoying it. There are 15 of us in the class. I'm friendly with a girl named Sophie. She's great [3]_____ we help each other study. Next year, we have to choose chemistry [4]_____ biology.

No, you're wrong about my apartment; it isn't near the university. It's about 30 minutes away. In the morning we can walk [5]_____ take a bus. The bus takes ten minutes. I have two roommates, Carlos [6]_____ Megan. They are brother and sister, [7]_____ they don't look like each other. Carlos is really nice. He's quiet [8]_____ has short black hair. Megan is very messy [9]_____ noisy.

Write soon.
Love,
Emma

---

1 Emma is enjoying college.   T / F
2 Emma thinks her classes are difficult.   T / F
3 Next year, Emma will study both chemistry and biology.   T / F
4 Emma lives near the university.   T / F
5 She can take a bus to get to the university.   T / F
6 Sophie is one of her roommates.   T / F
7 Carlos is Emma's brother.   T / F
8 Emma likes Carlos.   T / F

C Complete Emma's email in Exercise B with *and*, *but* and *or*.

WRITING PRACTICE

A PREPARE Imagine you receive an email from a friend asking you how you are. Write notes about:
- what you do
- where you live
- people you live, study or work with

B WRITE Use your notes to write an email to your friend.

PEOPLE   15

3.1 Days A typical day

VOCABULARY
Everyday activities

A Complete the paragraph with the verbs in the box.

get   get up   go   go   have
have   leave   read   take   watch

My name is Katia and I work as a news reporter. During the week, I ¹_____ really early in the morning because I ²_____ home at 4:15 am and ³_____ to work at 5 am. I don't ⁴_____ breakfast at home, but I ⁵_____ three cups of coffee at work to start my day. I finish work at noon and I usually ⁶_____ for a run and then go home. At home I ⁷_____ a shower and then ⁸_____ a book or ⁹_____ TV. In the evening I usually ¹⁰_____ to bed at 8:30 pm.

B Match the beginnings of the sentences (1–5) with the ends of the sentences (a–e).

1	We usually watch	a	to the news on the radio every morning.
2	Olivia often reads	b	coffee with friends from college after class.
3	Elaf always listens	c	for a walk on the beach on the weekend.
4	They usually go	d	something on Netflix in the evening.
5	I often have	e	the news on her phone.

GRAMMAR
Simple present positive

A Choose the correct options to complete the sentences.
1 I *live / lives* in an apartment in the center of the city.
2 My mother *watch / watches* TV every day.
3 My wife and I *listen / listens* to the same type of music.
4 She *work / works* in a clothing store in South Kensington.
5 He *have / has* breakfast with his family in the morning.
6 I think they *go / goes* to work by train.

B Complete the sentences with the correct form of the verbs in parentheses.
1 My friend _____ (*live*) in Los Angeles with his girlfriend.
2 We _____ (*get up*) early on the weekend and go for a run.
3 I always _____ (*have*) two cups of coffee in the morning.
4 He _____ (*work*) in a small office in the city center.
5 Tom _____ (*like*) to eat fruit for breakfast.
6 My sister _____ (*teach*) English in Hanoi, Vietnam.
7 David and Ahmet often _____ (*go*) swimming on the weekend.
8 Majid is an author. He _____ (*write*) science fiction books.

PRONUNCIATION
Third person -s

🔊 A Listen and complete the table with the verbs in bold.
3.1
1 Michelle **works** as a writer for a magazine.
2 She **lives** with her husband, Tim, in Washington D.C.
3 He **watches** American football on TV every Saturday.
4 Samantha **has** three cups of coffee in the morning.
5 She **goes** for a run every day after work.
6 My husband **starts** work at 5 am every day.
7 Emily **writes** for a famous fashion magazine.
8 He also **teaches** at the local university.

/s/	/z/	/ɪz/
works		

🔊 B Listen and circle the verb in each group that ends with a different sound.
3.2

1	(gets)	leaves	goes
2	washes	takes	teaches
3	works	plays	shows
4	looks	starts	watches
5	writes	comes	has

16 DAYS

3.2 Days — All day, every day

GRAMMAR
Adverbs of frequency

A Reorder the words to make sentences.

1. sleep / a night / I / for / eight hours / usually

   _____

2. late / class / Ali / for / always / are / and / Milos

   _____

3. always / Samantha / in the morning / of coffee / three cups / has

   _____

4. plays / sometimes / soccer / my brother / on the weekend

   _____

5. really / it / cold / in Thailand / never / is

   _____

6. video games / in the evening / often / play / I

   _____

B Use the information in the table to write eight sentences with adverbs of frequency.

	Emily	Ben
listens to music on the way to work	often	always
takes a shower in the morning	never	usually
plays video games on the weekend	rarely	sometimes
goes to yoga classes	always	rarely

1. *Emily often listens to music on the way to work*
2. _____
3. _____
4. _____
5. _____
6. _____
7. _____
8. _____

PRONUNCIATION
Word stress

🔊 Complete the table with the words in the box. Then listen and check.
3.3

| ~~breakfast~~ coffee director exercise interesting |
| Japan radio umbrella weekend yoga |

●●	●●	●●●	●●●
breakfast			

VOCABULARY
Prepositions of time

A Complete the paragraph with *at*, *in* or *on*.

I work as a writer so it is essential I have a routine. I always get up early ¹_____ the morning, but not ²_____ Sundays. That's my day to relax. In fact, usually ³_____ the weekend, I don't work, I go to the movie theater with my friends or go to the gym to exercise. Oh, and I never work late ⁴_____ night, I'm always too tired. ⁵_____ Wednesday afternoons, I sometimes go to the beach – it's beautiful there. Sometimes ⁶_____ the afternoon I take a nap; my wife thinks it's funny and says I'm like a little baby!

B Are the sentences correct or incorrect? Correct the mistakes.

1. My boss usually has meetings on the afternoon.
2. I never use my phone in night.
3. Maria usually goes shopping on the weekend.
4. Georgina sometimes goes for a run at Saturdays.
5. I usually take a shower early in the morning.
6. Ravi always finishes work early on Fridays.

DAYS 17

3.3 Days A special day

GRAMMAR
Simple present negative

A Choose the correct options to complete the paragraph.

This is a picture of me eating dinner with my family last year. Both of my parents were born in China, but they ¹*don't live / doesn't live* there anymore. They moved to Seattle, Washington, in the US when I was six. I still live in Seattle, but I ²*don't see / doesn't see* my parents very often. However, every year, they have a big party to celebrate Chinese New Year so I always go to stay with them for the weekend. Sadly, my brother usually ³*don't come / doesn't come* because he lives in Sweden now. The party is always great fun, but my dog Sparks ⁴*don't enjoy / doesn't enjoy* it, because he ⁵*doesn't like / don't likes* fireworks! He does like the food though. My mom loves making traditional dishes, but she ⁶*don't make / doesn't make* dumplings as she knows I ⁷*don't eat / doesn't eat* them.

B Are these sentences correct or incorrect? Correct the mistakes.
1 No, I don't live in the city center.
2 My father don't like science fiction movies.
3 She no listen to music at work.
4 My parents don't have a big house.
5 I not speak Spanish very well.

PRONUNCIATION
Sentence stress

🔊 Listen and underline the stressed words in each
3.4 sentence.
1 We always have a party on the 4th of July.
2 They don't put up decorations until December.
3 We open our presents in the morning.
4 There's a big parade in November.
5 My mother always makes traditional food.
6 Brad doesn't celebrate his birthday.

VOCABULARY
Big celebrations

Read the sentences and complete the crossword with the missing words.

Down
1 Do people wear … clothes to celebrate New Year's Eve in your country?
2 I always watch the … in Manhattan on the 4th of July.
4 My grandmother wants to have a big … to celebrate her 98th birthday.

Across
3 For Eid al-fitr we eat … food like kofta and shemai.
5 Lots of cities have … to celebrate Saint Patrick's Day. I love all of the dancers and costumes!
6 Do you give … to everyone in your family at Christmas?
7 We always put up … for Christmas. It makes the house look nice.

18 DAYS

3.4 Days — Reading

A DAY IN SPACE
By Simon Whittaker August 10, 2018

Chett Martins

What's a typical day like in space? We spoke to astronaut Chett Martins to find out.

CM: Do I have a daily routine? The answer is 'yes' – routine is important up here. It doesn't matter where we are, we always get up at the same time. The clocks here show the time back in Houston, Texas. The first thing we do is wash up. We don't have a shower, but it is important to stay clean, so we use liquid soap, water and a towel. After that, we have breakfast, then call mission control to talk about the plans for the rest of the day. We are always busy as there are lots of jobs to do. We usually work for 12 hours a day, so our days are really long.

After we finish work for the morning, we have lunch. In the past, food in space was terrible. Everything came in a tube and tasted disgusting! However, things have changed. Now we eat a lot of the same food we did back on Earth – fruit, vegetables, meat … However, most food is dried so you have to add water. We eat three meals a day and even have snacks like nuts and chocolate. After lunch, we spend a lot of time doing boring jobs like cleaning or making repairs to the equipment. It's also really important to exercise and most astronauts spend two hours a day running or cycling on special machines. I like to exercise in the afternoon after lunch.

That's it really. I love my job and I feel lucky to be one of a small group of people to do such an amazing job. After all, the view is out of this world!

READING

A READ FOR GIST Read *A day in space*. What does Chett Martins write about?

1 The things he does every day.
2 The things he does on special days.
3 The things he wants to do back home.

> **Glossary**
> **equipment (n)** the tools, machines, etc that you need for a particular job or activity
> **essential (adj)** very important or necessary
> **mission control (n)** a group of people who control a space flight from the ground
> **tube (n)** a long container that you squeeze to get thick liquids out

B READ FOR THE MAIN IDEAS Read the article again. Put Chett's daily routine in order.

___ call mission control
___ exercise
_1_ get up
___ have breakfast
___ have lunch
___ repair equipment
___ wash up

C READ FOR DETAIL Read the article again. Are these sentences true (T) or false (F)? Correct the false sentences.

1 Chett has a routine. T/F
2 After getting up he always takes a shower. T/F
3 Chett calls mission control to discuss the plans for the day. T/F
4 The food they eat comes out of tubes. T/F
5 Chett enjoys cleaning the space station. T/F
6 Astronauts usually exercise for an hour a day. T/F
7 Chett thinks he's lucky to be an astronaut. T/F

D REFLECT Answer the questions.

1 What things do you think might be difficult about being in space?
2 Would you like to have Chett's job? Why/Why not?
3 Do you think astronauts do an important job? Why/Why not?

3.5 Days

Listening; Functional Language

LISTENING

A LISTEN FOR GIST Listen to a conversation about a birthday. Check (✓) the activities Simon suggests.

- ☐ cook a meal at home
- ☐ go out to eat
- ☐ have a party
- ☐ watch a movie
- ☐ eat special food
- ☐ watch fireworks

B LISTEN FOR DETAIL Listen again. Complete the sentences with no more than three words from the conversation.

1 Beth's birthday is on _____.
2 Beth is _____ years old.
3 She doesn't think it's a _____ day.
4 She doesn't want a party because she doesn't like _____ of people.
5 Beth doesn't have a lot of _____.
6 Beth suggests they go to see a movie on _____ after work.
7 Simon says the first show is at _____.
8 Simon says he will _____ for 7:15.

C REFLECT Answer the questions.

1 Which of Simon's ideas do you like? Which don't you like? Why?
2 What do you usually do to celebrate your birthday?
3 Why do you think Beth doesn't want to celebrate her birthday?

FUNCTIONAL LANGUAGE
Making and responding to suggestions

A Complete the suggestions (1–4) and responses (a–d) with the words in the box.

about	awesome	great	how
let's	sounds	sure	why

1 _____ don't we go out to eat?
2 _____ about going to see that new Tom Hanks movie?
3 What _____ Friday evening after work?
4 _____ go to the one at 7:15.

a _____! I'll book the tickets for 7:15.
b I'm not _____. I don't have a lot of money.
c That _____ good. Hold on. Let me check what time it's showing.
d Now that's a _____ idea! I love Tom Hanks!

B Match suggestions (1–4) in Exercise A with responses (a–d).

C Listen and check your answers to Exercise B.

3.6 Days — Write a blog post about your day

A DAY in the LIFE of …

about | archive | contact

Mike Adamson, pilot at XEC Airlines
February 17, 2018 | Leave a comment

I work as a pilot so I don't really have a typical day. I do have a routine, but the times change when I'm in different places around the world.

Wherever I am, the first thing I do after I get up is have a cup of coffee. Before I get dressed I take a shower. After that, I check my flight schedule and have breakfast. I always have fruit and yogurt, as it is important to stay fit and healthy in my job.

I usually work three or four days a week. On the days when I don't work, I get up late. After breakfast, I often go to the swimming pool or gym. Then, I have lunch and take a nap. I like to relax in the afternoon and stay at home or in my hotel room.

When I'm working I take the subway to the airport and try to arrive early. I don't like to be late as my job is very difficult. Finally, after work I always read a book or talk to my wife and children on my computer. I enjoy my job, but I sometimes have to work at night and that isn't easy.

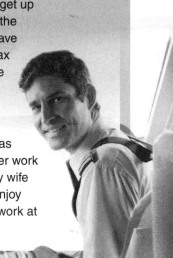

WRITING

A Read the blog post. What does Mike Adamson write about?

1 his work routine
2 his weekend routine
3 his new routine

B Read the blog post again and choose the correct options (a, b or c) to complete the sentences.

1 Mike says he doesn't have a …
   a schedule.   b routine.   c typical day.
2 He has a cup of coffee after he …
   a checks his schedule.   b gets up.
   c takes a shower.
3 He always eats fruit and yogurt …
   a three or four times a week.   b when he's working.
   c for breakfast.
4 He gets up late …
   a three or four times a week.   b when he's working.
   c when he isn't working.
5 He goes to the swimming pool or gym …
   a three or four times a week.   b when he's working.
   c when he isn't working.
6 When he goes to work at the airport …
   a he gets up early.   b he takes the subway.
   c he takes a nap.
7 He always tries to …
   a stay at home.   b talk to his wife and children.
   c work at night.

Glossary
nap (n) a short sleep, usually during the day
relax (v) to rest
schedule (n) a plan of activities and events and when they will happen

C Read the blog again and underline five sequencing words (e.g. *first, after that, then,* etc).

D Put Mike Adamson's daily routine in the correct order. Use the sequencing words that you underlined in Exercise C to help you.

___ check schedule   ___ take a shower
___ get dressed   ___ have breakfast
___ get up   ___ have lunch
___ go to the gym   ___ read a book
___ have a cup of coffee   ___ take a nap

WRITING PRACTICE

A PREPARE You are going to write a blog post about your daily routine. Complete the schedule with six to seven activities you do in a normal day and the times you do them.

Time	What?
___	get up and …
___	___
___	___
___	___
___	___
___	___

B WRITE Use your schedule in Exercise A to write a short blog about your day. Add details and use sequencing words (*first, after that, then* and *finally*) to explain the order.

4.1 Work and Education — What do you do?

VOCABULARY
Work and jobs

A Label pictures (1–8) with the jobs in the box.

> businesswoman   dentist   engineer   hairdresser
> journalist   mechanic   nurse   teacher

1 _____

2 _____

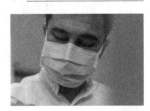
3 _____

4 _____

5 _____

6 _____

7 _____

8 _____

B Complete job descriptions (a–d) with the words in the box.

> computer   home   meet   meetings
> office   travels   wear

a My company has a large ¹_____ in central London, but I sometimes work from ²_____ to finish news stories.

b Samia ³_____ a lot for her job and often has ⁴_____ with people from other companies.

c I ⁵_____ lots of young people in my job and really enjoy helping them learn.

d Dan works in a hospital and he has to ⁶_____ a uniform. Sometimes he has to use a ⁷_____ to check information about his patients.

C Match each job description in Exercise B (a–d) with a job in Exercise A.

GRAMMAR
Simple present yes/no questions; short answers

A Match questions (1–6) with short answers (a–f).

1 Do you like your job?
2 Do you work at night?
3 Does your father work in the same office as you?
4 Do your parents know you work there?
5 Does your mother work from home?
6 Do you and your husband have children?

a No, she doesn't.
b No, we don't.
c Yes, I do.
d Yes, he does.
e No, I don't.
f Yes, they do.

B Complete conversations (1–4) with the correct form of *do* or *does*. Use contractions where possible.

1 **Andy:** _____ your brother like his new job?
   Ben: No, he _____.

2 **Charlie:** _____ you work 9 am to 5 pm?
   David: Yes, I _____.

3 **Emily:** _____ your sister study at a university?
   Fran: Yes, she _____.

4 **Greg:** _____ your parents work together?
   Harry: No, they _____.

C Reorder the words to make questions with *do* or *does*.

1 in / city / the / Do / center / work / you / ?
   Do you work in the city center?

2 full / sister / your / time / Does / work / ?
   _____

3 work / a / Do / at / uniform / you / wear / ?
   _____

4 wife / a / work / Does / travel / lot / your / for / ?
   _____

5 in / company / Does / have / an / your / New York / office / ?
   _____

PRONUNCIATION
Linking sounds: do/does

🔊 Listen and complete the questions with *Do you*, *Does she* or *Does he*.
4.1

1 *Do you* have to wear a uniform for your job?
2 _____ work at night?
3 _____ travel for your job?
4 _____ use a computer in his job?
5 _____ work in London?
6 _____ work from home?

22   WORK AND EDUCATION

4.2 Work and Education Good job!

GRAMMAR
have to / don't have to

A Complete the sentences with the correct form of *have to* and the verb in parentheses.

1 My brother's a firefighter, so he ___has to wear___ (*wear*) a uniform every day.
2 My brothers are both accountants, so they _____ (*wear*) a suit and tie every day.
3 A self-employed person _____ (*work*) nine to five.
4 Everything in the café is free – our employees _____ (*pay*) for food at work.
5 My sister starts work at 11 am. She _____ (*get up*) early.
6 My boss _____ (*travel*) a lot for her job. She often goes to foreign countries.

B Use the prompts to write questions with *have to*.

1 you / wear / a uniform at work?
   ___Do you have to wear a uniform at work?___
2 you / do a lot of / training?
   _____
3 you / work inside?
   _____
4 you / pay for tea and coffee?
   _____
5 you / work nine to five?
   _____

PRONUNCIATION
Connected speech: *have to*

🔊 Listen and complete the sentences with the verbs you hear.
4.2

1 Do you have to _____ the phone in your job?
2 Do you have to _____ from nine to five?
3 Does Sarah have to _____ a computer for her job?
4 When do you have to _____ work?
5 Does your boss have to _____ to lots of meetings?
6 What do you have to _____ in your job?

VOCABULARY
Time expressions

A Match the times (1–5) with the time expressions (a–e).

1 5:30 pm   a noon
2 12 pm   b early in the morning
3 9 am – 5 pm   c midnight
4 4:55 am   d late in the afternoon
5 12 am   e nine to five

B Complete the sentences with the time expressions in the box.

| early in the morning   late in the afternoon |
| midnight   nine to five   noon |

1 John starts work at 6 am every day so he has to get up really _____.
2 What time do you want to meet for lunch? Is _____ too early?
3 I have a really normal office job. I work from _____ with an hour for lunch.
4 OK, well don't stay out too late. Your father wants you home by _____.
5 Every Friday we have a meeting that starts at 2 pm and finishes _____.

WORK AND EDUCATION 23

4.3 Work and Education — Learn something new

GRAMMAR
Question words

A Complete the interview with the question words in the box.

| how long | how much | what | when |
| where | who | why | |

Dan: ¹_____ do you go to college?
Amy: I study at King's College, Cambridge.
Dan: ²_____ do you study there?
Amy: I study English literature.
Dan: ³_____ do you have classes?
Amy: On Mondays, Wednesdays and Thursdays.
Dan: … and ⁴_____ do you want to study English literature?
Amy: I want to be a famous author.
Dan: Oh, really? So, ⁵_____ is your favorite writer?
Amy: I like American writers like Donna Tartt and Jonathan Franzen.
Dan: ⁶_____ is your course?
Amy: Three years.
Dan: ⁷_____ does it cost?
Amy: Nine thousand dollars a year. It's very expensive!

B Write questions using the prompts in parentheses.

1 A: _____Where do you live?_____ (you / live?)
   B: I live in Kuala Lumpur in Malaysia.
2 A: _____ (you / do?)
   B: I work in a store during the day and I study English in the evening.
3 A: _____ (you / study English?)
   B: Because I want to train as a teacher.
4 A: _____ (take / to become a teacher?)
   B: It usually takes four years.
5 A: _____ (cost?)
   B: I don't know, but it's pretty expensive.

PRONUNCIATION
Word stress: questions

🔊 Listen to the questions and <u>underline</u> the stressed words.
4.3
1 Where do you study?
2 What do you study?
3 How long is your course?
4 Who is your teacher?
5 How much do you spend on books?
6 Why do you want to get a degree?

VOCABULARY
Education collocations

A Complete the paragraph with the verbs in the box. There is one verb you do not need.

| do | get | go | study | take | train |

Ha ha! This is a picture of me in the library. I'm from Jordan, but I moved to London last year to ¹_____ to college. I ²_____ medicine at King's College. It's a difficult course, and we have to ³_____ a lot of exams. That's why I'm always in the library! To ⁴_____ a medical certification, you also have to ⁵_____ in a hospital for three years – so that's seven years of studying! It's a lot of work, but I think it's worth it. When I'm finished, I can help people anywhere in the world.

B Cross out the incorrect noun in each group.

1 I don't like it when I have to take *a certification / an exam / a test*.
2 Why do you want to study *a degree / math / business*?
3 It's difficult to train as *a business / an engineer / a pilot*.
4 Sarah has to get *a degree / an exam / a certification* to work as a teacher.
5 Do you want to do *a course / a degree / a subject* in English?
6 My sister says she doesn't want to go to *college / a certification / a university*.

24 WORK AND EDUCATION

4.4 Work and Education — Reading

READING

A READ FOR GIST Read the job advertisement. Which picture (1–3) matches the ad?

Do you like nature?
Are you happy working outdoors?
We have the perfect job for you.

Marshall Nature Reserve is looking for a special person for the role of park ranger. Marshall Nature Reserve is on a remote island 2,000 miles from the nearest town or city, so it is important you like to spend time on your own.

The salary is $35,000 per year, but remember there are no stores and nothing to spend it on. We provide accommodations and food as well as three round-trip flights a year from the island to Cape Town, South Africa.

Usually a park ranger has to wear a uniform, but for this job it isn't necessary. You always have to get up very early in the morning, not only from Monday to Friday, but on the weekend as well. You have to work long hours but you don't have to worry about traffic jams or arriving late for work.

To apply contact Hans Coetze at h.coetze@marshall.org

B READ FOR KEY INFORMATION Read the ad again. Choose the correct options (a, b or c) to complete the sentences.

1 The nature reserve is …
  a on an island.   b in a town.   c in a city.
2 There aren't any … on the island.
  a people   b restaurants   c stores
3 The company does not pay for your …
  a accommodations.   b entertainment.   c flights.
4 You have to get up early …
  a every day.   b during the week.   c on the weekend.
5 Park rangers don't have to work …
  a outside.   b long hours.   c with other people.

C READ FOR DETAIL Read the ad again. Complete the sentences with no more than two words from the ad.

1 The ad is for the _____ of park ranger.
2 The island is _____ from any towns or cities.
3 Park rangers get paid _____ a year.
4 The company pays for three _____ a year.
5 Park rangers don't have to wear _____.
6 People who want to apply need to _____ Hans Coetze.

D REFLECT Answer the questions.

1 What is your perfect job? Why?
2 Would you apply for the job on the Marshall Island? Why/Why not?
3 What do you think is one advantage and one disadvantage of the job in the advertisement?

Glossary

accommodations (n) a place for someone to stay or live in
nature reserve (n) an area of land where animals and plants are protected
park ranger (n) reserve person whose job is to look after an area of land (e.g. a national park)
salary (n) an amount of money you are paid to do a job

WORK AND EDUCATION

4.5 Work and Education

Listening; Functional Language

LISTENING

A LISTEN FOR GIST Listen to an interview about work. Check (✓) the topics the speaker talks about.

- ☐ his current job
- ☐ the size of his company
- ☐ his work hours
- ☐ where he lives now
- ☐ where his office is
- ☐ what he eats for lunch
- ☐ the job he would like

B LISTEN FOR DETAIL Listen again. Are these sentences true (T) or false (F)? Correct the false sentences.

1 Graham works as an actor on TV. T / F
2 He works from home. T / F
3 He has to answer phones in his job. T / F
4 He works nine to five. T / F
5 He never has time for lunch. T / F
6 The company isn't very big. T / F
7 He thinks his job is very interesting. T / F
8 He wants to be a famous actor in Hollywood. T / F

C REFLECT Answer the questions.

1 Why do you think Graham works as a receptionist?
2 Do you think he should move to Hollywood? Why/Why not?

FUNCTIONAL LANGUAGE
Asking for someone and leaving a message

Put the conversation in the correct order. Then listen and check.

___ Receptionist:	Who's speaking, please?
___ Richard:	Yes, please. Can you ask her to call Richard from S-REK Ltd at 800-555-0199, please?
___ Receptionist:	Hold on a minute, please.
___ Richard:	Hello. Could I speak to Hannah Schmidt, please?
___ Receptionist:	I'm afraid she isn't available right now. Would you like to leave a message?
___ Receptionist:	Good morning. This is Schmidt and Brandt. Can I help you?
___ Receptionist:	I'm sorry, can you repeat that?
___ Richard:	It's Richard Kershaw.

> **Glossary**
>
> **greet (v)** to welcome someone with particular words or actions

4.6 Work and Education

Write an email asking for information

CAPE ACADEMY
Speaking classes | Exams | Private lessons

Do you want to [1]_____ a language or improve your language [2]_____?

We provide courses in [3]_____ languages – English, French, Spanish and Italian.

Choose a time that works for you. At Cape Academy, we offer classes in the [4]_____, afternoon and the evening.

For more information, [5]_____ Gabriella Souza at g.souza@language.net.sa

WRITING

A Complete the advertisement with the words in the box.

> contact four learn morning skills

B You are going to read a reply to the ad in Exercise A. Check (✓) the topics you think the writer will ask about. Then read and check.

- ☐ time of classes
- ☐ what books they use
- ☐ how much the classes cost
- ☐ computer skills
- ☐ the name of the teacher
- ☐ what languages they teach

To: g.souza@language.net.sa
Sent: February 17, 2018, 12:40 pm
From: p.hines@freenett.co.sa
Subject: Language classes

Dear Ms. Souza,

I am writing to ask about your language classes First what languages do you offer Do you have French classes Second, when are your classes I am free in the evenings and on the weekend Do you have classes on Saturdays or Sundays? Finally, how much does the course cost?

I look forward to hearing from you.
All the best,
Pieter Hines

C Read the email again. Correct six mistakes by adding question marks, commas and periods.

D Number the stages of the email in Exercise B.

- ___ Asking about the cost of the courses
- ___ Asking about the language courses on offer
- ___ Greeting and the name of the person you are writing to
- ___ Reason for writing
- ___ Standard 'end of letter' phrase
- ___ Asking about the times of classes on offer

WRITING PRACTICE

A PLAN Read the ad and write three or four questions you might ask.

> Two-day professional interview course.
> ## Learn how to be the perfect interview candidate.
> Courses run by our company experts.
>
> For more information, contact Ms. Petra Nagy at
> **p.nagy@professionaltraining.org**

B PREPARE Organize your questions into a plan for a formal email.

C WRITE Write your email. Use your plan to help you.

WORK AND EDUCATION 27

5.1 Places — There's no place like home

VOCABULARY
Rooms and furniture

A Label pictures (1–10) with the words in the box.

> armchair   bathtub   bed   oven   fridge   lamp
> shower   couch   toilet   dishwasher

1 _____

2 _____

3 _____   4 _____

5 _____   6 _____

7 _____   8 _____

9 _____   10 _____

B Complete the table with the words from Exercise A.

Bedroom	Bathroom	Kitchen	Living room

PRONUNCIATION
/b/, /d/ and /g/

🔊 Listen and (circle) the word you hear.
5.1

1 bad   dad
2 glue   blue
3 dig   big
4 gate   date
5 boat   goat
6 dot   got

GRAMMAR
there is / are

A Choose the correct options to complete the conversation.

Beth: This house is so strange. There ¹*is / are* a couch in the bedroom, but there ²*isn't / aren't* one in the living room.

Simon: Yes! It's weird. There ³*isn't / aren't* any chairs in the living room either.

Beth: ⁴*Is / Are* there a coffee machine in the kitchen?

Simon: Yes! There ⁵*is / are* two! And there are ⁶*any / some* plants.

Beth: Plants in the kitchen! Are there ⁷*any / some* plants in the other rooms?

Simon: No, there aren't ⁸*any / some* plants in the other rooms.

Beth: OK … this is strange. There ⁹*is / are* a fridge in the living room.

Simon: A fridge?

Beth: Yes, and there ¹⁰*is / are* two lamps next to it.

B Complete the paragraph with *there is*, *there isn't*, *there are* and *there aren't*.

Day 14 of 30:
My favorite room
JENNA THOMPSON | August 14, 2018 | 128 COMMENTS

My favorite room in my apartment is the living room. ¹_____ two comfortable chairs and ²_____ a big couch. ³_____ a table because the room is too small, but ⁴_____ some lamps. ⁵_____ a TV across from the couch and ⁶_____ some books on a bookshelf. ⁷_____ any plants in the living room, but we have some in the kitchen.

5.2 Places — My neighborhood

VOCABULARY
Places in a town or city

A Complete the definitions with the places in the box.

> café   gym   library   movie theater   museum
> park   subway station   supermarket

1. _café_ a place where you can buy tea, coffee and cake
2. _____ a large area with grass and trees
3. _____ a place where you can watch movies
4. _____ a place where you can look at or borrow books
5. _____ a place where you can catch a train
6. _____ a large store that sells food
7. _____ a place where you can exercise
8. _____ a place where you can see old, important objects

B Label the pictures with the words in the box.

> airport   hospital   market   restaurant   stores   theater

1 _____

2 _____

3 _____

4 _____

5 _____   6 _____

GRAMMAR
can

A Look at the pictures. Write sentences using the correct form of *can* and the words in parentheses.

(Lizzie / speak / Spanish)   (he / ride / a bike)

1 _____   2 _____

(she / sing)   (he / swim)

3 _____   4 _____

(he / make / sushi)   (Sarah / play / violin)

5 _____   6 _____

B Are these sentences correct or incorrect? Correct the mistakes.

1. We go can't to the movie theater tonight because it's closed.
2. It's amazing that you can't swim! Can your sister swim?
3. David can to speak three languages, English, French and Korean. His mom is French and his dad is South Korean.
4. I'm sorry! You can't borrow this book from the library. You can read it here.
5. She lives close to her office so she can walks to work in the morning.
6. I play guitar and I'm in a band. Do you can play a musical instrument?

PRONUNCIATION
Weak forms: *can/can't*

🔊 Listen to the sentences. Is the pronunciation of *can / can't* strong or weak?
5.2

1. Can you speak another language?   strong / weak
2. Yes, I can.   strong / weak
3. Can Danny speak Chinese well?   strong / weak
4. No, he can't.   strong / weak
5. But he can speak Japanese very well.   strong / weak
6. Emily can't speak any other languages.   strong / weak
7. Can they both speak French and Italian?   strong / weak
8. Yes, they can.   strong / weak

5.3 Places — Amazing buildings

GRAMMAR
Imperatives

A Match situations (1–5) with imperatives (a–e).

1 ___ You are at the movie theater. The person in front of you is making a lot of noise.

2 ___ You are visiting a museum and want more information from the guide.

3 ___ You don't know how to use the coffee machine. Your friend is with you.

4 ___ Someone is running by the swimming pool. There is a no running sign next to them.

5 ___ You are with a friend. You see something amazing, but your friend isn't looking.

a Look at that!
b Please be quiet.
c Please don't run.
d Please help me.
e Tell me more.

B Complete the sentences with the verbs in the box.

be   buy   go   listen   push
take   touch   turn

1 _____ the lights off when you leave.
2 _____ to this – an octopus has three hearts!
3 Elliott, don't _____ your sister!
4 Turn left, then _____ straight until the end of the road.
5 Please _____ your shoes off at the door.
6 _____ a travel guide before you go.
7 Don't _____ anything children. It's all very expensive.
8 Sit down and _____ quiet!

VOCABULARY
Adjectives to describe the appearance of things

Complete the descriptions with a, e, i, o or u.

The Hayward Gallery is a ¹m__d__rn building in London. A lot of people think it looks ²t__rr__bl__. They say it's ³__gly and should be knocked down!

The Sydney Opera House is an ⁴__m__z__ng building. It looks ⁵b_____t__f__l with the ⁶str__ng__ shape of its roof. Some people think it looks like a sailing ship.

PRONUNCIATION
Word stress: adjectives

🔊 Listen and (circle) the adjective with a different stress pattern in each group.
5.3

1	big	(boring)	old
2	modern	ugly	beautiful
3	friendly	amazing	terrible
4	small	cool	ugly
5	interesting	modern	funny
6	popular	terrible	strange

5.4 Places — Reading

Apartments and houses to rent

Stunning three-bedroom house

a House to rent with three bedrooms, a kitchen, living room, bathroom (no bathtub), a garage and a small yard. The rent is $2,100 per month. The house is close to some stores and there is a gym and a library just a five-minute walk from the house.

Modern studio apartment

b A studio apartment. One bedroom, fully equipped kitchen and living space with couch and table. There is a shower and a shared utility room with washing machine and dryer. It is ten minutes by bus to the city center from the apartment. The rent is $1,350 per month.

Four single rooms available

c Four individual rooms for rent in a large house. These are suitable for students or young professionals. There is a shared kitchen, bathroom and living room. All the bedrooms have locks. $700 + utility bills (water, electricity, internet) per person.

Two-bedroom apartment in a central location

d A modern, two-bedroom apartment in a great location across from a beautiful park and close to restaurants, a supermarket and five minutes from a subway station. From the station it is just 30 minutes by train to the city center. There is also on-street parking for a car. This is a perfect apartment for a young family.

Glossary

studio apartment (n) a small apartment that only has one main room

READING

A READ FOR SPECIFIC INFORMATION Read the ad. Which ad (a–d) matches the floorplan?

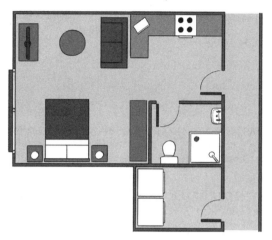

B READ FOR SPECIFIC INFORMATION Read the ad again. Check the correct ad(s) for each question.

	a	b	c	d
1 Which place has two bedrooms?				
2 Which place is just ten minutes away from the city center?				
3 Which place doesn't say how much the rent is?				
4 Which two places have stores nearby?				
5 In which place do you pay extra for electricity?				
6 Which two places have information about a place to park a car?				
7 Which place is not good for more than one or two people?				
8 In which two places do you share rooms with other people?				

C READ FOR DETAIL Read the ad again. Complete the sentences with no more than three words from the ad.

1 The three-bedroom house costs _____ a month.
2 It's a five-minute walk from a library and a _____.
3 In the studio apartment, there's a _____ and a dryer in the utility room.
4 The apartment is a ten-minute _____ trip from the city center.
5 Each room in the four-bedroom house has a _____ on the door.
6 Rent doesn't include utility _____ (water, electricity and internet).
7 The two-bedroom apartment is five minutes away from a _____.
8 It doesn't come with a garage, but there is _____ parking.

D REFLECT How would you describe where you live in an ad?

PLACES 31

5.5 Places — Listening; Functional Language

LISTENING

A LISTEN FOR KEY WORDS Listen to a conversation about neighborhoods. Check (✓) the topics that are discussed.
- ☐ places to eat
- ☐ local sports clubs
- ☐ street art
- ☐ tourism
- ☐ markets
- ☐ transportation in the city
- ☐ shopping centers
- ☐ parks and green spaces

Glossary
fashionable (adj) popular at a specific time

B LISTEN FOR DETAIL Listen again. Are these sentences true (T) or false (F)? Correct the false sentences.
1. Hannah thinks Camden market is amazing. T / F
2. There aren't any nice restaurants in Camden. T / F
3. Camden is very busy on the weekend. T / F
4. Victor lives in France. T / F
5. There is a park close to where Victor lives. T / F
6. There isn't any street art in Montreal. T / F
7. There aren't any old buildings in Montreal. T / F
8. Both Montreal and Camden are popular with tourists. T / F

C REFLECT Discuss the questions.
1. How do these two places compare to where you live?
2. How would you describe where you live? What's it like?

FUNCTIONAL LANGUAGE
Asking for and giving directions

A Match the beginnings of the sentences (1–6) with the ends of the sentences (a–f).

1. Go straight
2. Turn
3. Go to the end
4. Go past
5. Take the second
6. My apartment is next

a. the café.
b. of the road.
c. ahead.
d. turn on the right.
e. to the movie theater.
f. left.

B Put the conversation in the correct order.

☐ **Victor:** Movie theater on the right …

☐ **Hannah:** OK. Come out of the subway station. There is a bank across from the entrance.

☐ **Victor:** First turn on the right …

[2] **Hannah:** Oh, hey Victor! Do you need directions to my apartment?

[1] **Victor:** Hi Hannah! I'm at the subway station.

☐ **Hannah:** No, on the left. Walk to the end of the road. My apartment is on the left next to the café.

☐ **Victor:** … across from the subway station.

☐ **Hannah:** Walk past the movie theater. It's on the left.

☐ **Victor:** Yes, please.

☐ **Hannah:** Cross over the road and turn left. Then take the first turn on the right.

C Listen and check your answers to Exercise B.

5.6 Places — Write a description of a place

WRITING

A Read *Paro Taktsang: The Tiger's Nest*. Match the description to the correct picture (1–3).

Paro Taktsang: The Tiger's Nest
A beautiful building in the mountains of Bhutan

Paro Taktsang, or the Tiger's Nest, is a famous building in Bhutan near northern India. The building is high up on the side of a mountain. There are amazing views across the valley below. The old building has white walls, and beautiful red and gold roofs that you can see from far away.

Paro Taktsang has eight main buildings that are all old caves. Inside the buildings you can see lots of paintings and some statues. You can't take photos inside the building, but you can take photos outside.

There is a long walk to reach Paro Taktsang. It takes around five hours to get there and back. The walk is interesting with lots of things to see. About halfway up there is a beautiful waterfall. There are not a lot of tourists at Paro Taktsang, so it is nice and quiet and it is a great place to visit.

B Read the article again and (circle) the adjectives.

C Write questions for these answers.

1 _____What is the building called?_____
Paro Taktsang.

2 _____
In Bhutan.

3 _____
It's a beautiful building with white walls and red and gold roofs.

4 _____
You can see paintings inside and visit a beautiful waterfall.

5 _____
It is nice and quiet and a great place to visit.

WRITING PRACTICE

A PLAN Choose a famous building and write notes about the following:
- what it's called
- where it is
- what it looks like
- what you can see or do there
- your opinion

B PREPARE Organize your notes into paragraphs. Try to add extra information.

C WRITE Use your plan to write a short description. Remember to use adjectives to make your writing more interesting.

6.1 That's Entertainment — Let's go out

VOCABULARY
Entertainment

A Label pictures (1–6) with the words in the box.

> movie theater   comedy show   concert   exhibit   festival   theater

1 _____   2 _____   3 _____

4 _____   5 _____   6 _____

B Complete the sentences with the words from Exercise A.

1 There's a new art _____ on at the Tate Modern. Do you want to go with me?
2 My parents try to go to the _____ once a month to see plays like *Macbeth* and *Romeo and Juliet*.
3 Every Friday, we go to our local _____ to watch a movie. The tickets are half price, so it's a great evening out!
4 My favorite _____ is *Secret Solstice* in Iceland. Lots of amazing bands play there every year.
5 Busy week? Need a laugh? Come to our weekly _____ with some of the best comedians around.
6 We have two tickets for a _____ with the Beijing Orchestra. I'm really excited about it.

PRONUNCIATION
Word stress: noun patterns

 Listen and circle the correct stress pattern.
6.1

1 concert   (Oo)/ oO
2 music   Oo / oO
3 photograph   Ooo / oOo
4 entertainment   Oooo / ooOo
5 movie   Oo / oO
6 costume   Oo / oO

GRAMMAR
Likes and dislikes

A Correct the mistakes in each sentence.

1 I don't like stay in all the time!
2 I loves go to the movie theater.
3 They loves to playing soccer.
4 He not like watch TV.
5 I hates pizza!
6 We not like visit museums.

B Look at the table. Write six sentences about Ahmad with *love*, *like*, *don't like* or *hate* and a verb.

☺☺	soccer on TV / festivals
☺	Italian food
☹	video games
☹☹	theater / pop music

1 *Ahmad loves watching soccer on TV.*
2 Ahmad _____
3 He _____
4 _____
5 _____
6 _____

34 THAT'S ENTERTAINMENT

6.2 That's Entertainment — It was fun

GRAMMAR
was/were

A Reorder the words to make sentences and questions.

1 your / where / born / were / parents / ?

2 busy / this / my / really / train / morning / was

3 was / Tokyo / month / in / I / business / for / last

4 expensive / tickets / really / were / the / !

5 last / concert / was / how / the / night / ?

6 terrible / was / really / movie / a / that / !

7 week / it / hot / really / last / all / was

B Complete the conversation with *was*, *were*, *wasn't* and *weren't*.

Mike: That [1]___was___ great. You know I love great comedy.

Alan: Well, the first two comedians [2]_____ very funny, but the third one [3]_____.

Mike: No, that's true. She [4]_____ terrible; the people in the club [5]_____ laughing at all.

Alan: I guess she [6]_____ brave to stand up there and keep going.

Mike: No, that [7]_____ stupid.

Alan: That [8]_____ a nice thing to say. I'm sure all the comedians [9]_____ trying their best.

Mike: I know, but it [10]_____ fairly expensive to get in.

Alan: True, but we [11]_____ there for three hours so it [12]_____ too bad.

PRONUNCIATION
Weak forms: *was/were*

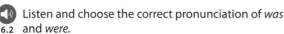
Listen and choose the correct pronunciation of *was* and *were*.

1 That was a really great concert. /wəz/ /wʌz/
2 Yes, it was. /wəz/ /wʌz/
3 Were there lots of people? /wər/ /wɜːr/
4 Yes, there were. /wər/ /wɜːr/
5 Were your friends at the concert? /wər/ /wɜːr/
6 Yes, they were. /wər/ /wɜːr/
7 It was fairly expensive. /wəz/ /wʌz/
8 Yes, it was really expensive. /wəz/ /wʌz/

VOCABULARY
Past time expressions

A Complete the paragraph with *in*, *ago* or *last*.

This is a picture of my aunt, the famous Japanese actress, Fumi Watanabe. She was born [1]_____ 1978 and appeared in her first movie [2]_____ 1986 at the age of just 8. Two years [3]_____, she won an award for her acting and she was very proud. [4]_____ month she was nominated again and she hopes to win for a second time. The awards take place [5]_____ the winter and it is always really cold. She called me twenty minutes [6]_____ to tell me she has tickets to the event for the whole family. I'm so excited.

B Are the sentences correct or incorrect? Correct the incorrect ones.

1 The first Oscar ceremony was last 1929.
2 They were at the movie theater in night.
3 Were you at home last weekend?
4 There was a concert two nights ago.
5 Peter was at college five years last.
6 There's a great music festival here in July.

6.3 That's Entertainment — Life stories

GRAMMAR
Simple past regular and irregular verbs

A Complete the paragraph with the correct form of the verbs in the box.

> be   begin   die   make   move
> reach   release   start   win   work

David Bowie ¹_____ born in London on January 8, 1947. At the age of 13, he ²_____ to learn the saxophone. In 1969, the song *Space Oddity* ³_____ number 5 in the UK music charts. Six years later, Bowie ⁴_____ to Los Angeles and ⁵_____ his movie career with a performance in the movie *The Man Who Fell to Earth*. Over the next few years, Bowie ⁶_____ on a number of different projects and in 1979 ⁷_____ his first theater performance on Broadway. Over his 50-year career, Bowie ⁸_____ six Grammys for his music and 25 awards in total. In January 2016, Bowie ⁹_____ at the age of 69 just two days after he ¹⁰_____ his last album, *Blackstar*.

B Complete the sentences with the simple past form of the verb in parentheses.

1 We _____ (*take*) lots of photos on our trip to Hawaii.
2 I _____ (*go*) to see the new *Star Wars* movie at the Roxy last night.
3 Paolo _____ (*move*) to Los Angeles last year to become an actor.
4 My father _____ (*buy*) me a new camera for my birthday.
5 I _____ (*see*) a great comedian on TV last night, but I can't remember her name!
6 The *Bergen International Film Festival* in Norway _____ (*start*) in 2000.
7 Junko _____ (*meet*) her husband five years ago.
8 Leonardo DiCaprio _____ (*win*) an Oscar for Best Actor in 2016.

PRONUNCIATION
Simple past regular endings

🔊 Listen to the simple past verbs. Is the final sound /d/, /t/ or /ɪd/? Circle the correct sounds.

1 hated   /d/ /t/ /ɪd/
2 helped   /d/ /t/ /ɪd/
3 looked   /d/ /t/ /ɪd/
4 married   /d/ /t/ /ɪd/
5 performed   /d/ /t/ /ɪd/
6 played   /d/ /t/ /ɪd/
7 practiced   /d/ /t/ /ɪd/
8 started   /d/ /t/ /ɪd/

VOCABULARY
Life events

Complete the life events (1–8) with the verbs in the box.

> became   got   had   moved
> started   studied   was   went

1 Ella _____ to Oxford University where she met Mark.

2 Mark and Ella both _____ languages at the university.

3 Mark _____ work as a journalist after attending the university.

4 Ella _____ a famous actress after attending the university.

5 Mark and Ella _____ married in the summer of 2002.

6 They _____ to a new house in 2004.

7 Their son, Jacob, _____ born the following year.

8 Mark and Ella _____ three children, Jacob, James and Jack.

6.4 That's Entertainment — Reading

THIS WEEK AT THE MOVIES
• JORDAN STEVENS | May 4, 2018 | 899 COMMENTS

3200 (PG-13)
This movie is set in the future and the story is about the lives of a boy and his sister. I usually don't like this type of movie, but the two young actors, Damian Shultz and Greta Simons, were amazing as the boy and girl. The story is good and you don't know what is going to happen next and this keeps you interested the whole time. This is a movie to go and see in the movie theater.

Laugh Night (PG-13)
I love to laugh, so I was very excited when I went to the movie theater. In the end, I wasn't happy. I saw the trailer and thought the movie looked great. I knew one of the actors, Tosh Ellis, and liked his last two movies, but he wasn't good in this one. I think I laughed twice in the 90 minutes, not very good when a ticket costs $8. Watch the trailer, but not the movie, as that's about as good as it gets!

The Blade (NC-17)
One of the best movies of the year, but that isn't a surprise. Emma Davies won an Oscar last year and was great in this movie. The director, Ivan Rodriguez, is excellent and I love all his movies! I also loved the special effects. It's the type of horror movie people will love or hate, but that's always the way with this genre. The only problem was the end wasn't very good, but I thought the movie was awesome!

Glossary
director (n) the person who tells the actors what to do when they make a movie
genre (n) a type of book, movie or music
special effects (n) the sounds and images in a movie made with technology, for example with computers
trailer (n) an ad for a movie or a TV show that shows a small part of the movie or show

READING

A READ FOR GIST Read the movie reviews. Then match the name of a movie with a summary of the writer's opinion (1–3).
1 A funny trailer, but a bad movie. _____
2 Another movie from a great director. _____
3 A good movie to see at the movie theater. _____

B READ FOR DETAIL Read the reviews again. Are these sentences true (T) or false (F)? Correct the false sentences.
1 The writer thought the acting in *3200* was good.   T / F
2 The writer doesn't recommend *3200*.   T / F
3 The writer usually likes movies that make him laugh.   T / F
4 The writer thought *Laugh Night* was funny.   T / F
5 The writer was surprised that *The Blade* was so good.   T / F
6 The writer thinks that not everyone likes horror movies.   T / F

C SCAN Scan the reviews again. Complete the sentences with names from the text.
1 _____ won an Oscar for a different movie.
2 _____ and _____ are both young actors.
3 The writer loves movies directed by _____.
4 The writer liked other movies that _____ was in.

D REFLECT Answer the questions.
1 What was the last movie you saw at the movie theater?
2 What was the movie about?
3 Did you enjoy it? Why/Why not?
4 Which of the three movies (*3200*, *Laugh Night*, *The Blade*) would you like to see? Why?

6.5 That's Entertainment
Listening; Functional Language

LISTENING

A LISTEN FOR KEY WORDS Listen to a conversation about a movie. Number the topics in the order they are discussed.

- ☐ The actors
- ☐ The director
- ☐ The music
- ☐ The special effects

B LISTEN FOR DETAIL Listen again and answer the questions.

1. What did Silvia think of the actors?
   - a They were awful.   b They were great.
   - c She isn't sure.
2. What does Luke describe as awesome?
   - a the actors   b the special effects
   - c the story
3. Who does Meryl Adams play in the movie?
   - a the mother   b the sister   c the daughter
4. What did Rick think was awful?
   - a the director   b the music
   - c the special effects
5. Who or what does Luke describe as amazing?
   - a Meryl Adams   b the music   c the director
6. Who doesn't think the director could win an Oscar for this movie?
   - a Rick   b Luke   c Silvia

C REFLECT How do you choose the movies you watch?

FUNCTIONAL LANGUAGE
Asking for and giving opinions

Complete the conversation with the words in the box. Then listen again and check.

> about   awesome   awful   ~~great~~
> hate   loved   OK   sure   think

Luke: So what did you think of the movie?
Silvia: Honestly, Luke. It wasn't [1] _great_.
Luke: Really? I [2] _____ it! I thought the actors were great.
Silvia: What do you mean? I thought they were [3] _____.
Luke: That's not true. How [4] _____ you, Rick?
Rick: I'm not [5] _____.
Luke: What? Come on. The special effects were [6] _____!
Rick: Yes, that's true, but you also need good actors and an interesting story.
Luke: I loved the actors. Meryl Adams was great as the mother.
Silvia: That's true, but the other actors were terrible.
Luke: Rick, what do you [7] _____?
Rick: Uh, some of the acting was [8] _____, but generally I think I agree with Silvia … and the music was awful.
Luke: What? I love that type of music.
Rick: I know you do, but I [9] _____ it.
Luke: What about the director? He's amazing.
Rick: Hmm … I don't know. He hasn't won an Oscar, has he?
Luke: No, that's true, but he could win one for this movie.
Silvia: Ha ha! Now I know you're joking!

6.6 That's Entertainment — Write a review of an event

Laura M

★★★★☆ 10 days ago
Day of the 'killer' tomato

a I went to my first festival in Spain in 2010 and every year try to go to a new one somewhere in Europe. Last year, I went to the famous La Tomatina festival in Buñol near Valencia with three of my friends.

b We bought tickets for a three-day tour and we stayed in a hotel in Valencia. The ticket cost $175, but that included the hotel for three nights, so I think it was a fairly good value.

c Buñol is about 38 km from Valencia, so first we woke up early and drove to the town. We got to the Plaza del Pueblo in the center of the town at around 10 am. Next, at about 11 am, a water cannon was fired into the crowd. Then, people started picking up tomatoes and throwing them at each other. You have to squash the tomatoes in your hand before you throw them so they don't hurt anyone.

d The whole event lasted an hour. It finished when another water cannon was fired. After that, we tried to find somewhere to clean up. We were lucky as we found someone with a big hose. Finally, we found a café to have lunch and laugh about the day.

e I thought it was really fun – almost 20,000 people having a big fight with tomatoes! Next year I want to go to the Cheese Rolling in England.

WRITING

A Look at the picture. What do you think happens at the event?

B Read the review. Check your ideas from Exercise A.

C Read the review again. Are these sentences true (T) or false (F)? Correct the false sentences.

1 Laura went to the festival alone. T / F
2 The hotel cost $175 per night. T / F
3 They stayed in Buñol. T / F
4 The event started at 11 am. T / F
5 The event takes about three hours. T / F
6 She plans on going to a different festival next year. T / F

D Scan the review again. Match topics (1–5) with paragraphs (a–e).

1 Details of the event ___
2 The writer's opinion ___
3 Background ___
4 Cost of the event ___
5 How the event ends ___

E Scan the review again and <u>underline</u> the narrative sequencers (*then, after that*, etc).

F Put the events of the story in the correct order. Use the narrative sequencing words to help you.

___ Next, actors dressed in 1920s costumes showed us to our seats.
___ Finally, we watched the end of the movie. It was a great night.
___ First, we waited in the line to get into the venue.
___ After that, we had dinner while a live band played music from the movie.
___ Then, we watched the first half of the movie.

WRITING PRACTICE

A PREPARE Think of an event that you went to and write notes about the topics in Exercise D.

B WRITE Use your notes to write a review. Use narrative sequencers to organize your ideas.

THAT'S ENTERTAINMENT 39

7.1 Travel and Transportation — Getting around

VOCABULARY
Transportation

A Match pictures (1–6) with the words in the box.

> bicycle   ferry   plane   taxi
> trolley   subway   train

1 _____

2 _____

3 _____

4 _____

5 _____

6 _____

B Complete the types of transportation in sentences (1–6).

1 We took a small **b** __ __ __ to the island.
2 Tom always feels nervous before he flies on a **p** __ __ __ __ __.
3 My sister was five when she learned to ride a **b** __ __ __ __ __ __.
4 When we visited San Francisco last year, we traveled around the city by **t** __ __ __ __ __ __ __.
5 There's a **b** __ __ stop right outside my house!
6 Mike fell off his **m** __ __ __ __ __ __ __ __ __, but he was OK because he always wears a helmet.

PRONUNCIATION
/eɪ/ and /oʊ/

🔊 Complete the table with the words in the box. Then listen and check.
7.1

> boat   coach   main   motorcycle
> phone   plane   same   train

/eɪ/	/oʊ/

GRAMMAR
could

Look at pictures (1–6) and complete the sentences with *could* or *couldn't*.

1 Sophie _____ read before she started school.

2 Five years ago, Callum _____ swim.

3 I _____ speak Japanese when I first moved to Tokyo.

4 Fifty years ago, you _____ buy a car for under $1,000.

5 When she was young, Emily _____ run really fast.

6 I had trumpet lessons when I was ten, but _____ play very well.

40 TRAVEL AND TRANSPORTATION

7.2 Travel and Transportion
A love of adventure

VOCABULARY
Travel phrases

A Cross out the incorrect noun in each group.

1 We were late so we missed the *bus / travel / train*.

2 Ana returned *home / from New York / the flight* last week.

3 They were really excited when they arrived *the scooter / at the hotel / in Hong Kong*.

4 Susi and Dewi decided not to take *the hotel / the ferry / a taxi* as it was too expensive.

5 We left *the station / the motorcycle / for Seoul* 30 minutes late.

B Complete the review using phrases from Exercise A.

> ★☆☆☆☆ 1 day ago
> ## American nightmare
> Mark T
>
> We ¹_____ last night. Unfortunately, the whole vacation was terrible. The guidebook said it wasn't a good idea to ²_____ from the airport to the city center as traffic is bad and it's expensive.
>
> When we finally ³_____ in Manhattan, the receptionist told us we couldn't check in for another four hours!
>
> The next morning we ⁴_____ to go on the sightseeing tour, and so we had to go on our own. We wanted to see the Statue of Liberty. Unfortunately, we ⁵_____ 30 minutes late and missed the last ferry of the day. We were so unlucky!

GRAMMAR
Simple past negative

Rewrite the sentences in the simple past negative.

1 I watched the news this morning.
   I didn't watch the news this morning.

2 Mae studied German at school.
   _____

3 I saw Simon and Alison at the party on Saturday.
   _____

4 I went to the gym after work.
   _____

5 I liked math when I was in school.
   _____

6 Lizzie finished the report yesterday.
   _____

7 I spoke to him after the meeting.
   _____

8 Molly enjoyed that movie last night.
   _____

PRONUNCIATION
Word stress: cities

🔊 <u>Underline</u> the stressed syllable in each city. Then listen
7.2 and check.

1 <u>Pa</u>ris
2 Bangkok
3 Berlin
4 Caracas
5 Milan
6 Kathmandu
7 Lisbon
8 Manila
9 Mumbai
10 Chicago

7.3 Travel and Transportation — A trip to remember

GRAMMAR
Simple past questions

Complete the conversation with the simple past form of the verbs in parentheses. Add question words where necessary.

Karen: Hi Sabrina. [1] _____Was_____ (be) it your birthday on Saturday?

Sabrina: Oh, hey Karen. Yes, it was.

Karen: [2] _____ (go) to a restaurant with your family?

Sabrina: No, I had a party.

Karen: Oh, really? I didn't get an invite on Facebook …

Sabrina: Oh, sorry. I thought you were on vacation last week.

Karen: I was, but I got back on Friday. Don't worry. So, [3] _____ (have) the party?

Sabrina: At my house. We sat in the yard because the weather was so good.

Karen: Oh, that sounds nice. So, [4] _____ (eat)?

Sabrina: We had a barbecue and my sister-in-law brought some of that nice ice cream from that store near the movie theater.

Karen: Oh, wow! That stuff is delicious. So … [5] _____ (be) Tom at the party?

Sabrina: No, he wasn't. He had to work all weekend.

Karen: [6] _____ (take) any photos?

Sabrina: Of course. Do you want to see them?

Karen: Sure. Wow! It's really dark. [7] _____ (do) the party end?

Sabrina: Uh … about midnight I think. My dad was worried about complaints from the neighbors.

PRONUNCIATION
Connected speech

🔊 Listen to the questions and sentences. Draw a ‿ between words that are linked together.
7.3

1 What did you do on the weekend?
2 How long did you work there?
3 They stayed there for two weeks.
4 Susan didn't want to go home.
5 Did you have fun?
6 Where did you go last summer?
7 Did you stay in a hotel?
8 We went to a lot of museums.

VOCABULARY
Verb phrases

Look at the pictures. Complete the sentences with an appropriate simple past verb.

1 I _____ shopping with Emily on Saturday.

2 Tim _____ lost and had to ask directions.

3 I _____ a lot of interesting people at the party on Saturday.

4 Ji Yeon and I _____ some great food at the street market on Sunday.

5 Bea _____ a lot of photos on vacation in Italy last summer.

7.4 Travel and Transportion — Reading

Three **amazing** ways to work in **another country**

Want to live in another country for a few months, but don't have the cash? Here's how to start your adventure.

a 'WWOOFING'

Lots of farms around the world are part of a project that lets people learn about life on a farm for free. If you like animals and the countryside, then you will love it – just be prepared to wake up at 6 am and work outside in all kinds of weather! Many people make very close friends with the other workers as the ¹**destination** usually isn't near a city, meaning you spend all of your free time together. Another important ²**detail** is that you will only be paid for your hard work through free meals and somewhere to sleep; if you want to save money, this isn't for you.

b Tour Guide

Do you know a lot about a place in another country? Perhaps you could find a job as a tour guide taking other visitors around and showing them all the ³**sights**. You need to know about the history of the place and be able to remember lots of information. You can also learn a lot from the other tour guides, as sometimes they know lots of ⁴**fascinating** facts. You will get paid for your work and you can also make extra from the ⁵**tips** that people give you at the end of each tour.

c Working in a hostel

Hostels are ⁶**budget** hotels where people can stay when they visit a new place. When people stay in a hostel they sometimes ⁷**share** a bedroom and showers. There are lots of different jobs in a hostel that are similar to the ones in a hotel. You can find work as a receptionist or helping to clean the rooms. It is often possible to find work in a hostel, especially during the ⁸**peak season** when the hostels can be full of people. When you work you will be paid, but some of your money will go toward paying for your room and meals.

READING

A READ FOR GIST Read *Three amazing ways to work in another country*. Match pictures (1–3) to jobs (a–c).

B IDENTIFY MEANING FROM CONTEXT Read again. Choose the correct meaning of the words in bold.

1   a the place you're going
    b a place where you stay
2   a everything you need to know about something
    b one small piece of information
3   a places you can buy things
    b interesting places that people go to see
4   a very interesting
    b fairly surprising
5   a extra money someone gives you
    b extra information about something
6   a not very expensive
    b very expensive
7   a to want something that belongs to someone else
    b to use something at the same time as another person
8   a the time of year when many people visit a place
    b a time of year when a place isn't very busy

C READ FOR DETAIL Read the article again. Choose the correct jobs to complete the sentences.

1 You don't get paid any money working as a *farm worker / tour guide / hostel worker*.
2 There are different jobs you can do as a *farm worker / tour guide / hostel worker*.
3 You need to know facts about the place to work as a *farm worker / tour guide / hostel worker*.
4 When you work as a *farm worker / tour guide / hostel worker* you spend a lot of time talking to people.
5 You won't get all of your money when you work as a *farm worker / tour guide / hostel worker* and stay there as well.
6 When you work as a *farm worker / tour guide / hostel worker* you start very early in the morning.
7 Working as *farm worker / tour guide / hostel worker* you don't usually work in a city.

D REFLECT Would you like to go on a working vacation? Why/Why not?

7.5 Travel and Transportation

Listening: Functional Language

LISTENING

A LISTEN FOR GIST Listen to an interview about a journey around the world. Mark the route on the map.

B LISTEN FOR DETAIL Listen again. Are these sentences true (T) or false (F)? Correct the false sentences.

1. Tom didn't want to travel anywhere by plane. T/F
2. He traveled from Paris to Athens by train. T/F
3. He bought a motorcycle in Nairobi. T/F
4. It took three weeks to get from Singapore to the US. T/F
5. Tom says he met some very unusual people. T/F
6. He says it was strange to stay in hotels in the US because they were so normal. T/F

C REFLECT Answer the questions.

1. What do you think of Tom's journey?
2. Would you like to go on a similar journey? Why/Why not?
3. What do you think would be the most interesting part of the journey? Why?

FUNCTIONAL LANGUAGE
Checking in and out of a hotel

Complete the conversation with the words in the box. Then listen and check.

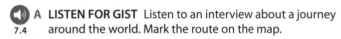

afternoon   checkout   help   included
passport   password   reservation   wi-fi

Receptionist: Good ¹_____, sir. How can I help you?

Tom: I have a ²_____ for a double room for two nights.

Receptionist: OK, great. Could I have your ³_____, please?

Tom: Of course. Here you are. What time is ⁴_____ on Sunday?

Receptionist: It's at noon, sir.

Tom: Great, and is breakfast ⁵_____?

Receptionist: Yes, it is. It's between 6:30 and 10 am in the dining room. Do you need any ⁶_____ with your bags?

Tom: No, I'm fine thank you. Is there ⁷_____ in the rooms?

Receptionist: Yes, there is. The ⁸_____ is on the desk in your room.

Tom: OK, great. Thank you.

Receptionist: You're welcome, sir. Do you need anything else?

Tom: Uh … yes. Can I have my key?

44 TRAVEL AND TRANSPORTATION

7.6 Travel and Transportion

Write a short article about a travel experience

TRAVEL SPOTLIGHT:
SIEM REAP

Last December I went to Siem Reap in Cambodia with my husband. ¹___, so it seemed like the perfect choice.

Siem Reap is a fairly big town with lots of places to eat and stay. Of course, there are expensive hotels, but we couldn't afford one of those. ²___

There are lots of activities and interesting places to see and visit, so you won't be bored! ³___ It was a great way to sightsee in a short time. We also both enjoy shopping and there were lots of stores to buy souvenirs. So every day was completely different!

For me it was a great vacation because I did all the things I enjoy and the weather was sunny but not too hot. ⁴___ There were a lot more tourists than I thought there would be.

WRITING

A Read *Travel spotlight: Siem Reap*. Complete blanks (1–4) by choosing sentences (a–e). There is one extra sentence that you do not need.

   a We chose a small family-run place and met some really friendly people.

   b We went to a different restaurant every evening and we ate some really nice food.

   c We are both really interested in history and it is close to the famous temples of Angkor Wat.

   d Probably the only thing that we didn't like was that the temples were crowded.

   e On one of the days, we went on a bike tour around the city.

B Read the article again. Complete the sentences with no more than two words from the text.

   1 The writer went to Siem Reap in _____.

   2 She couldn't afford to stay in an _____.

   3 While she was there, she did some sightseeing and shopped for _____.

   4 She describes the weather as sunny, but not _____.

   5 She didn't enjoy the temples because there were a lot of _____ there.

C Complete the sentences with *so* and *because*.

   1 We went in February _____ it isn't as hot as other times of the year.

   2 There were lots of cheap stores _____ we bought lots of souvenirs.

   3 We don't usually go on long flights _____ we are both frightened of flying.

   4 I didn't really enjoy the museums _____ they were full of tourists.

   5 We didn't have time to see everything, _____ we both want to go back there again.

WRITING PRACTICE

A **PLAN** You are going to write about a travel experience. Write notes about:

- where you went
- where you stayed
- what you did there
- what the weather was like
- what you liked/didn't like

B **WRITE** Use your notes to write a short article/blog entry. Use *so* and *because* to join your ideas.

8.1 Food and Drink — I'm hungry!

VOCABULARY
Food and drink

A Look at the pictures and complete the crossword.

(Crossword with 1 Down = c-h-i-c-k-e-n)

DOWN

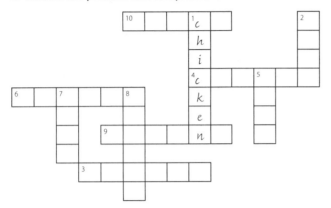
1

2

5

7

8

ACROSS

3

4

6

9

10

GRAMMAR
Countable and uncountable nouns; *some* and *any*

A Find and correct eleven mistakes in the blog post below.

Health goals
JENNA THOMPSON | October 23, 2018 | 97 COMMENTS

This week, I'm trying to be healthier. So instead of snacks like a bar of chocolate, I'll eat any fruit, like a apple, a banana or some oranges. I never eat breakfast, but this morning I had a bowl of cereal with milks and a toast without some butter.

At lunchtime, I went to a café close to where I work. I ordered some brown rices with chicken and a glass of juices. Then for dessert I had some yogurt.

In the evening, I usually have some sandwiches, but this evening I'm going to have some fishes with a vegetables and any cheeses and biscuits.

B Complete the table with the words in the box.

> apple   banana   cookie   chips   hamburgers
> mushroom   pasta   potatoes   rice   sandwiches
> toast   yogurt

Countable singular	Countable plural	Uncountable

PRONUNCIATION
Plurals

🔊 8.1 Listen and circle the word with a different plural ending sound in each group.

1 potatoes   hamburgers   chips
2 oranges   sausages   tomatoes
3 carrots   peas   nuts

46 FOOD AND DRINK

8.2 Food and Drink What we eat

VOCABULARY
Containers

Cross out the incorrect noun in each sentence.

1 Can you go and get a can of *beans / soup / rice* for me?
2 Can you buy a big carton of *milk / sparkling water / apple juice* at the store?
3 I'd like two packages of *chocolate cookies / chips / yogurt* please.
4 We need one more jar of *chocolates / coffee / sauce*.
5 Can you buy a box of *chocolates / sauce / cereal* on your way home?
6 We also need to get a bottle of *yogurt / orange juice / milk* for your grandmother.

PRONUNCIATION
Short and long vowel sounds

Listen and write the words you hear in the correct circle.
8.2

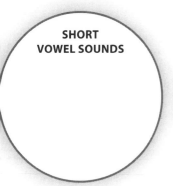
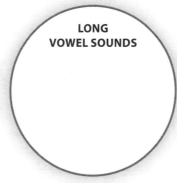

GRAMMAR
much, many, a lot of

A Complete conversations (a–e) with *much*, *many* and *a lot of*.

a
Peter: You'll never guess how ¹_____ Juan's new car was ... $50,000!
Carla: That's ²_____ money!

b
James: How ³_____ people are coming to our barbecue tonight?
Tom: About 35. So we'll need ⁴_____ food.

c
Jacob: How ⁵_____ pasta do we have?
Rick: Uh, there's ⁶_____ rice, but no pasta.

d
Alex: Our teacher gave us ⁷_____ homework to do tonight.
Sam: That's OK because there aren't ⁸_____ days left before our test.

e
Toni: How ⁹_____ sugar do you take in your tea?
Eleanor: I don't take very ¹⁰_____, just half a teaspoon.

B Are these sentences correct or incorrect? Correct the incorrect ones.

1 How many bread do you usually eat?
2 We have a lot of eggs in the fridge.
3 Karen drinks much coffee in the morning.
4 How much milk do you have in your coffee?
5 There aren't much bananas left. Can you buy some?
6 How much people did you invite to the party?

FOOD AND DRINK 47

8.3 Food and Drink — Yes, chef!

GRAMMAR
a/an, the, no article

A Choose the correct options to complete the rules.

1 We use *a or an* / *the* when we talk about a singular noun for the first time.
2 We use *a or an* / *the* with plural nouns when it is clear what we are talking about.
3 We use *the* / *no article* when we talk about things in general.
4 We use *the* / *no article* with singular nouns when there is only one.
5 We use *a or an* / *no article* with the names of people and things, cities and most countries.

B Complete the text with *a/an*, *the* or no article.

Bradley Cooper
American actor, director and producer

Bradley Cooper was born in [1]_____ Philadelphia in 1975. He is [2]_____ actor who has been in [3]_____ movies such as *Silver Linings Playbook* and is also [4]_____ voice of [5]_____ Rocket Raccoon in *Guardians of the Galaxy*. He is famous all over [6]_____ world, but one thing you might not know about him is that he is [7]_____ excellent cook. He said in [8]_____ interview that he learned many skills from playing [9]_____ chef in [10]_____ TV show *Kitchen Confidential* and [11]_____ movie *Burnt*. [12]_____ TV show was based on [13]_____ book by Anthony Bourdain, who was also from [14]_____ US.

PRONUNCIATION
Consonant clusters

🔊 Listen and <u>underline</u> the consonant clusters in these words.
8.3
1 flour
2 fruit
3 healthy
4 bottle
5 vegetables
6 fry
7 bowl
8 sandwich

VOCABULARY
Food preparation

A Choose the correct verbs to complete the recipe.

Easy pancakes recipe

INGREDIENTS
100 g flour
300 ml milk
2 large eggs
1 tbsp oil
Pinch of salt
Sugar/lemon for serving

METHOD

1 *Peel* / *Put* / *Serve* the flour, milk and some salt into a bowl.
2 *Chop* / *Crack* / *Fry* two eggs into the mixture.
3 *Beat* / *Fry* / *Put* the mixture together and leave for 30 minutes.
4 *Add* / *Crack* / *Heat* some oil in a frying pan.
5 Put some of the mixture into the pan and *beat* / *fry* / *heat* on each side for one minute.
6 *Chop* / *Put* / *Serve* with some sugar, lemon juice or maple syrup.

B Complete the sentences with the words in the box.

add chop fry grate peel put serve

1 Can you _____ a banana, for me?
2 Why don't you _____ some cheese on the top before you put it in the oven?
3 _____ all the eggs in the bowl.
4 When it's ready to eat, _____ it with some bread.
5 Put some oil in the pan and _____ the mushrooms for about four minutes.
6 To make the sauce, _____ some tomatoes into small pieces.
7 _____ some salt and pepper to make everything taste nice.

48 FOOD AND DRINK

8.4 Food and Drink — Reading

Trying something new

JENNY MACKINTOSH | November 12, 2018 | 658 COMMENTS

I love food, and when I go on vacation, I try to eat local food that is **unique** to the area. Of course, I always look for the healthy options, but I also try to find 'strange' food. I know that for the people that live there the food probably isn't strange, but it's not the type of food I'm used to.

Last year in Cambodia I was traveling down a road and saw a man serving food from a stand. I stopped and looked; he was cooking **frogs**! I know they eat these in some countries, but it was my first time – they were delicious and **tasted** a little like chicken! Later on, I went to a restaurant where everything was made from insects. I can't say that everything was nice and, in fact, some of it was terrible, but I tried it.

In Japan I ate some fish that was **poisonous**, and I had a soup in China that was made with poisonous mushrooms, too. Both dishes were delicious, but I don't think I would eat them again as I was nervous the whole time!

The funny thing is I'm from Scotland and we eat some strange food there. I'm not talking about the food we fry, but one dish in particular – Haggis. This is made from the **stomach** of a sheep and we often eat it with *tatties*, a name we give to potatoes, and *neeps*, which are a kind of vegetable. I love it!

READING

A READ FOR GIST Read *Trying something new*. Choose the best title.
1 Great food
2 Unusual food
3 Terrible food

B READ FOR DETAIL Read the blog post again. Choose the correct options (a, b or c) to complete the sentences.

1 When Jenny is on vacation she tries to find and eat food that …
  a she likes.
  b is unhealthy.
  c she doesn't usually eat.

2 When Jenny ate frogs she thought they …
  a tasted delicious.
  b were chicken.
  c were not from Cambodia.

3 She went to a restaurant where you could only eat …
  a local food.
  b food where insects were one of the ingredients.
  c soups.

4 In Japan and China she ate dishes …
  a made from fish.
  b made from mushrooms.
  c that were delicious.

5 One of her favorite dishes is …
  a fried.
  b Haggis.
  c a type of vegetable.

C SCAN Scan the post again. What part of speech (noun, adjective or verb) are the words in bold?
1 unique _____
2 frog _____
3 taste _____
4 poisonous _____
5 stomach _____

D DECODE Read again. Match definitions (a–e) with the words in Exercise C (1–5).
a to have a particular flavor
b the part of your body where food goes after it's eaten
c like no other
d a small animal with long back legs that lives in water
e causing death or illness if eaten

E REFLECT Would you eat any of the food described in the blog?

FOOD AND DRINK 49

8.5 Food and Drink — Listening; Functional Language

Glossary

spicy (adj) spicy food has a hot flavor

LISTENING

A LISTEN FOR GIST Listen to a conversation about food. Who likes the food in pictures (1–3) – Oli or Tara?
8.4

B LISTEN FOR DETAIL Listen again and answer the questions.
8.4

1 What does Tara say about hot dogs and burgers?
   a She eats them all the time.
   b They are very healthy.
   c She thinks they are delicious.

2 What does Oli think about hot dogs and burgers?
   a They are delicious.
   b They are unhealthy.
   c They are healthy.

3 What does Tara usually eat?
   a hot dogs
   b salads
   c Thai food

4 What does Oli say about his favorite Thai dish?
   a It's hot and spicy.
   b It's made with coconut milk.
   c It's delicious with rice.

5 What type of food do Oli and Tara go to eat?
   a Italian
   b American
   c Thai

6 How does Tara describe the slices at the pizza place?
   a delicious
   b great
   c enormous

C REFLECT Are you more like Oli or Tara? Why?

FUNCTIONAL LANGUAGE
Ordering food in a restaurant

A Match the beginnings of the sentences (1–6) with the ends of the sentences (a–f).

1 Are you ready …   a mango juice with ice?
2 Yes, I'll have …   b to drink?
3 OK. Would you like something …   c the dessert menu?
4 Could I have a …   d the chicken salad, please.
5 Would you like to see …   e bill, please?
6 No, thanks. Can I have the …   f to order?

B Listen and check your answers to Exercise A.
8.5

50 FOOD AND DRINK

8.6 Food and Drink — Write an online restaurant review

★★★★★ 2 days ago
Meow
Haruto

I love cake and cats, so I was very happy when I found this café that has both of ¹**them**! Basically, you can order something to eat and hold or play with a cat at the same time. One of the cats was so nice I wanted to take ²**him** home. My waitress was very helpful and ³**she** told me to order the chocolate cake and tea with milk – ⁴**they** were both amazing! ⁵**It**'s very popular so go before lunchtime.

WRITING

A Read the review of a cat café. What do the pronouns in bold refer to?

1 _cake and cats_
2 _____
3 _____
4 _____
5 _____

★★★☆☆ 3 days ago
At Night
Ralph S

At Night is a special restaurant where everything is dark! My girlfriend and I couldn't read the menu, but our waiter told us what was on ¹the menu. I ordered pasta. ²The pasta was not easy to eat with no light. ³The pasta was delicious though. My girlfriend ordered a mushroom dish and a vegetable side dish as ⁴my girlfriend doesn't eat meat. Unfortunately, ⁵the mushroom dish and the vegetable side dish were cold, so my girlfriend wanted to ask the waiter to take ⁶the mushroom dish and the vegetable side dish back to the kitchen. The only problem was ⁷my girlfriend couldn't see ⁸the waiter!

B Read the review of an unusual restaurant. Replace the underlined nouns with a suitable pronoun.

1 _____ 5 _____
2 _____ 6 _____
3 _____ 7 _____
4 _____ 8 _____

C Read the second review again and answer these questions.

1 Who did Ralph go to the restaurant with?
2 Why couldn't they read the menu?
3 What did the writer order?
4 What was his food like?
5 Why didn't his girlfriend enjoy her meal?

WRITING PRACTICE

A PREPARE You are going to write a review about an usual restaurant or café. Write notes about:

- the name of the restaurant or café
- who you went with
- the food you ate
- what was unusual about the restaurant
- the waiter / waitress

B WRITE Use your notes to write a review. Remember to use pronouns in your writing.

FOOD AND DRINK   51

9.1 Shopping — People watching

VOCABULARY
Clothes

Match the words in the box to pictures (1–4).

> boots (x2)　cap　coat　jacket (x2)　jeans (x3)
> scarf　skirt　sneakers　socks　sunglasses　sweater

PRONUNCIATION
/ɜːr/

🔊 Underline the /ɜːr/ sound in these words. Then listen
9.1 and check.

1 skirt
2 prefer
3 nurse
4 earn
5 work
6 girl
7 person
8 learn

GRAMMAR
Present progressive

A Complete the conversation with the present progressive form of the verb in parentheses. Use contractions where possible.

Anna: Hi Sally, what ¹ _are you doing_ (you / do)?
Sally: Right now I ² _____ (look) at a dress.
Anna: Oh, so ³ _____ (you / shop).
Sally: Yes, ⁴ _____ (Sara / help) me find something for my interview tomorrow.
Anna: ⁵ _____ still _____ (we / have) lunch?
Sally: Yes, we are, don't worry! ⁶ _____ (leave) soon.
Anna: ⁷ _____ (Ben / come) too or ⁸ _____ (work) today?
Sally: No, ⁹ _____ (work). We'll see you in an hour.

B Use the prompts to write present progressive questions.

1 he / ride / a bike
  _____
2 he / eat / pizza
  _____
3 she / play / piano
  _____
4 they / run / in the park
  _____

C Look at images (1–4) and write short answers to the questions in Exercise B.

1 _____   2 _____

3 _____   4 _____

52 SHOPPING

9.2 Shopping — Job swap

VOCABULARY
Present time expressions

A Complete the texts with the time expressions in the boxes.

> at the moment   these days   today

1 _____, I'm studying a lot as I have exams next week. But 2 _____, I'm relaxing at the beach. I'll study when I go home later 3 _____.

> currently   now   right now

Luca, come downstairs 4 _____! We need to clean up the apartment. David called me saying he picked up Grandma just 5 _____ and they are 6 _____ driving over here.

B Choose the correct options to complete the sentences.
1 I'm *currently / today* in a meeting and unable to take your call.
2 I would like that report *right now / these days*!
3 I'm wearing a coat *these day / today* because it's cold.
4 I'm going swimming *now / at the moment* because it's hot.
5 I love reading, but *these days / today*, I spend more time doing yoga.
6 *At the moment / Now*, I'm feeling really fit and healthy.

GRAMMAR
Simple present vs present progressive

A Complete the sentences with the simple present or present progressive form of the verbs in parentheses.
1 I sometimes _____ (*work*) in a local charity store.
2 She _____ (*not help*) out at her daughter's school today.
3 What _____ (*they / watch*) right now?
4 They _____ (*ride*) their bikes everywhere.
5 Rob usually _____ (*walk*) to work.
6 Why _____ (*you / leave*) now? It's too early.
7 This week we _____ (*not close*) the store until 7:00 pm every night.

B Are the following sentences correct or incorrect? Correct the incorrect ones.
1 You should wear a scarf – it snows outside.
_____
2 We aren't usually playing tennis every day.
_____
3 Jamie is calling Rachel right now.
_____
4 Are you usually going to the beach?
_____
5 Max is writing an email at the moment.
_____
6 She isn't currently cook in the kitchen.
_____
7 Are they walk to school?
_____

PRONUNCIATION
/ŋ/

 Listen and (circle) the words that have the /ŋ/ sound.
9.2
1 sung
2 walking
3 sunglasses
4 pink
5 younger
6 sandwich
7 jeans
8 strong

SHOPPING   53

9.3 Shopping — Shop till you drop

GRAMMAR
Object pronouns

A Complete the table.

Subject pronoun	Object pronoun
I	me
he	
she	
it	
we	
you	
they	

B Replace the underlined words with the correct object pronoun.

1 I'm going for a walk with my cousin. Do you want to come with <u>my cousin and me</u>?
2 The phone is really cheap. Why don't you just buy <u>the phone</u>?
3 Are those jeans new? How much did you pay for <u>those jeans</u>?
4 There's a new Marvel movie at the movie theater. Have you seen <u>the new Marvel movie</u>?
5 That's a nice shirt. Your father would like it. Why don't you buy it for <u>your father</u>?
6 Stephanie is my best friend. Would you like to meet <u>Stephanie</u>?
7 What time are you and Maria leaving? I might leave with <u>you and Maria</u>.

VOCABULARY
Stores and services

A Complete the definitions with the words in the box.

| bank   dentist's   department store |
| hairdresser's   pharmacy |

1 _____ a place where you get your teeth checked
2 _____ a place where you can buy medicine
3 _____ a place where you keep your money
4 _____ a large store divided into lots of different parts
5 _____ a place where you can get your hair cut

B Complete the paragraph with the words in the box.

| bakery   bookstore   butcher's   department store |
| library   market   newsstand   ~~supermarket~~ |

I grew up in a village. It didn't have a ¹ _supermarket_ so we went to the ² _____ to buy fresh bread, then to the ³ _____ to get some meat. At the local ⁴ _____, there were stands selling fruits and vegetables. There wasn't a ⁵ _____, but we could borrow books from the local ⁶ _____ for free. My dad always bought his paper from the ⁷ _____. For clothes and things for the house, we went to the big ⁸ _____ in the nearest town, which was 30 kilometers away.

PRONUNCIATION
/tʃ/ and /ʃ/

🔊 Are the underlined sounds /tʃ/ or /ʃ/? Listen and choose the
9.3 correct sounds.

1 <u>ch</u>eese   /ʃ/   /tʃ/
2 <u>sh</u>oes   /ʃ/   /tʃ/
3 fa<u>sh</u>ion   /ʃ/   /tʃ/
4 que<u>st</u>ion   /ʃ/   /tʃ/
5 <u>s</u>ure   /ʃ/   /tʃ/
6 sta<u>ti</u>on   /ʃ/   /tʃ/
7 na<u>tu</u>re   /ʃ/   /tʃ/
8 wa<u>sh</u>   /ʃ/   /tʃ/

9.4 Shopping — Reading

Meet Joe Taylor

The 'perfect job'?
September 15

What a day! When I applied for the 'perfect job', I expected it to be easy. Yes, I'm enjoying it, but it's hard work. I usually wake up at around 6:00 am and go for a walk along the beach; it sounds nice, but actually at that time of the morning it can be fairly cold, and when it's raining it's not much fun. These days the weather is nice, but a month ago it was **terrible** every day. Today, I walked all the way to the far end of the island – that's about five kilometers, so it's a fairly long way. Currently, I'm writing my diary entry for the day, **uploading** some photos and checking my emails.

Tired of walking
September 16

5:30 am, Wow! Right now I'm sitting down and eating my breakfast. Last night I couldn't really sleep because it was very windy. Today, I have to walk around the island and check all the buildings to see what **damage** there is. When I first arrived here I thought it would be great living somewhere with no motorcycles or cars, but today I would love to be able to get on a motorcycle and not have to walk everywhere. It's days like today when I don't want to do this job anymore …

Hard work
September 19

I know I'm **supposed to** write my diary entry every day, but sometimes there isn't enough time. The last few days were **crazy**. When I got back to my room I was too tired to do anything apart from take off my clothes and fall into bed. At the moment I'm **organizing** things for today and tomorrow before I go outside to start work. I'm feeling **under pressure** at the moment, but I'm sure everything will be fine in the end.

READING

A READ FOR GENRE Read the blog posts and answer the questions.

1 Where is it from?
 a A magazine article
 b An online blog
2 Who is he writing for?
 a People interested in his job
 b People looking for a new job

> **Glossary**
> **be supposed to (adj)** used to show that you don't believe something that many others do
> **expected (adj)** likely to happen or be true

B READ FOR SPECIFIC INFORMATION Read the blog posts again. Complete the sentences with no more than three words from the blog posts.

1 Joe thought the job would _____ when he applied for it.
2 After waking up in the morning he usually goes _____.
3 He doesn't think it's _____ when the weather is bad.
4 Because of the wind he couldn't _____.
5 He doesn't like having _____ because he doesn't have any transportation.
6 There isn't always _____ to write a diary entry.
7 He thinks that _____ everything will be fine.

C DECODE Scan the posts again. Complete definitions (1–6) with the words in bold.

1 _____ physical harm to something so it is broken and needs repairing
2 _____ preparing or arrange an activity or event
3 _____ sending documents or photos from your computer to the internet
4 _____ not sensible or practical
5 _____ feeling stressed because you have too much to do
6 _____ very bad

D REFLECT Answer the questions.

1 Do you think the job sounds like fun? Why/Why not?
2 What type of job do you think it is?
3 Do you know any unusual jobs?

9.5 Shopping — Listening; Functional Language

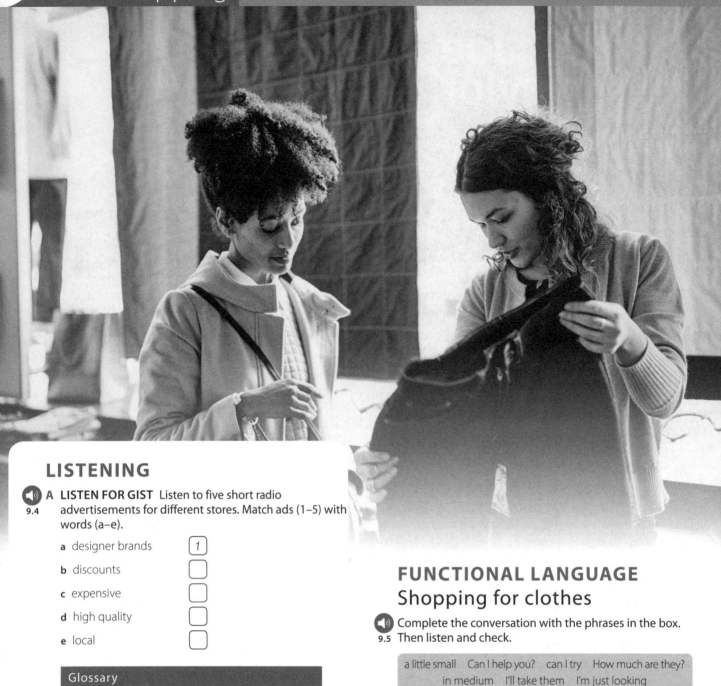

LISTENING

A LISTEN FOR GIST Listen to five short radio advertisements for different stores. Match ads (1–5) with words (a–e).

a designer brands [1]
b discounts [ ]
c expensive [ ]
d high quality [ ]
e local [ ]

Glossary

in stock (phrase) when something is 'in stock', it is available in the store to buy immediately

B LISTEN FOR DETAIL Listen again. Are these sentences true (T) or false (F)? Correct the false sentences.

1 Max Out isn't open at the moment. T / F
2 Max Out doesn't have any bargains. T / F
3 JCs sells different products every week. T / F
4 Products at Bargains 2day are low quality. T / F
5 Clothes at Tuffin are expensive, but good quality. T / F
6 You can only buy ties at TieUp. T / F

C REFLECT Answer the questions.

1 Where do you usually buy your clothes?
2 Do you look for bargains and discounts?
3 Which of the five stores would you like to visit? Why?

FUNCTIONAL LANGUAGE
Shopping for clothes

Complete the conversation with the phrases in the box. Then listen and check.

> a little small   Can I help you?   can I try   How much are they?
> in medium   I'll take them   I'm just looking
> look really great   the changing rooms

Store clerk: Good morning. ¹_____?
Customer: No, ²_____, thank you. Oh! Actually, ³_____ these jeans on, please?
Store clerk: Of course, ⁴_____ are over there.
Store clerk: Oh! They ⁵_____ on you …
Customer: Thank you, but I think they are ⁶_____. Do you have the same style ⁷_____?
Store clerk: Yeah, here you are.
Customer: These are perfect. ⁸_____?
Store clerk: They're $35, but there's a 10% discount.
Customer: Oh, great! ⁹_____.

56 SHOPPING

9.6 Shopping — Write a social media post

1. **Hannah**
   1 hr ago

   It's Sunday morning and we're go for our usual walk through the woods. I love picking wild mushrooms. You have to be careful as some are in danger, but there are lots that are delicious. Rick is trying to climb a tree … he's crazy!

2. **Mae**
   45 mins ago

   Hi, I'm down at the sports center with my friends rock climbing. We're having a grate time and trying to see how high we can get. It's my first time doing it and it's amazing! I' am happy we're inside. As we don't have to worry about the weather.

3. **Luke**
   33 mins ago

   We're traveling down to London to watch a play? We're taking the train as it's more relaxing. Jenny is playing a game on her tablet and Simon is listening to music. mom packed some sandwiches for us. so we're all eating those. More later.

WRITING

A Read the three social media posts. Which one matches the picture?

B Read the three posts again. Choose the correct names to complete the sentences.

1 *Hannah / Mae / Luke* is doing something for the first time.
2 *Hannah / Mae / Luke* is doing something they usually do.
3 *Hannah / Mae / Luke* is going somewhere to do something later.
4 *Hannah / Mae / Luke* writes about finding food.
5 *Hannah / Mae / Luke* is eating something at the moment.
6 *Hannah / Mae / Luke* is doing something that is done outside.

C Read the posts again. Find and correct eight mistakes.

WRITING PRACTICE

A PREPARE You are going to write a social media post. Write notes about:
- a picture you would use
- where you are
- who you are with
- what you are doing
- how you are feeling

B WRITE Use your notes to write your post.

C REVIEW Check your work for mistakes.

SHOPPING 57

10.1 The Great Outdoors — The right location

VOCABULARY
Landscape features

Look at the pictures and complete the descriptions with the words in the box. Change the form if necessary.

> beach   desert   forest   hill   island   jungle
> lake   mountain   ocean   river

This is a picture of Bled in Slovenia. It is famous for its beautiful ¹_____ with an ²_____ in the center. Around the town you can see a ³_____ and some snowy ⁴_____.

Malaysia has many white sand ⁵_____. This one is special though. The ⁶_____ is so clear and in the background you can see ⁷_____ covered in ⁸_____, where you can go hiking if you're feeling adventurous!

This is one of my favorite places in Egypt. I love sailing down the ⁹_____ with the empty ¹⁰_____ all around us.

GRAMMAR
Comparatives

A Write the comparative form of these adjectives.

1. big — *bigger*
2. old — _____
3. easy — _____
4. famous — _____
5. good — _____
6. cheap — _____
7. close — _____
8. expensive — _____
9. dirty — _____
10. bad — _____
11. comfortable — _____
12. strange — _____

B Rewrite the sentences using the opposite of the adjective in bold. The meaning of the sentence should be the same.

1. Sandra is **quieter** than Julia.
   Julia is louder than Sandra.
2. I find geography **easier** than science.
   _____
3. The ocean was **colder** than the swimming pool.
   _____
4. Juan's apartment is **smaller** than my house.
   _____
5. The weather in the spring is **cloudier** than in the summer.
   _____
6. Her second novel was **worse** than her first.
   _____

PRONUNCIATION
Weak forms: /ə/ in *than*

🔊 Listen and complete the sentences with no more than
10.1 two words.

1. My new car is much _____ my last one.
2. This part of the city is _____ where I live.
3. Mount Everest is _____ Ben Nevis.
4. My father is four years _____ my mother.
5. The Nile is _____ the Amazon.
6. This shirt is more _____ the one online.

58   THE GREAT OUTDOORS

10.2 The Great Outdoors — Where on Earth?

VOCABULARY
Seasons and weather

Complete the words in the text. Use the first letter in bold to help you.

Japan: When to go and what to pack

¹S_____ (March to May) is the best time of year to go as the weather is ²s_____ and you can see the amazing cherry blossom trees. It can still be a little ³w_____ so pack a sweater.
⁴S_____ (June to August) is fairly ⁵h____, but it often ⁶r_____ in June. You should wear light clothes that dry quickly!
⁷F____ (September to November) can be ⁸f_____ especially in the hills. Remember to bring a jacket!
⁹In the w_____ (December to February) it ¹⁰s_____ a lot in the mountains and by the ocean and it can get very ¹¹c_____. Wear boots and a scarf!

PRONUNCIATION
/oʊ/ and /aʊ/

🔊 Are the underlined sounds /aʊ/ or /əʊ/? Listen and circle
10.2 the correct sounds.

1 cl**ou**dy   /oʊ/   /aʊ/
2 c**oa**t   /oʊ/   /aʊ/
3 m**ou**ntains /oʊ/   /aʊ/
4 l**ow**   /oʊ/   /aʊ/
5 t**oe**   /oʊ/   /aʊ/
6 **ou**tside   /oʊ/   /aʊ/
7 n**ow**   /oʊ/   /aʊ/
8 ph**o**ne   /oʊ/   /aʊ/

GRAMMAR
Superlatives

A Complete the table.

Adjective	Comparative	Superlative
tall	taller	tallest
dry		
hot		
kind		
busy		
bad		
crowded		
ancient		
good		

B Use the prompts to write superlative sentences and questions.

1 Russia / big / country / in the world.
   Russia is the biggest country in the world.

2 The Volga / long / river / Europe.
   _____

3 La Paz in Bolivia / high / capital city / world.
   _____

4 The mosquito / dangerous / insect / world.
   _____

5 Finland / happy / country / world.
   _____

6 What / fast / car / world?
   _____

7 What / wet / season?
   _____

8 Who / good / friend?
   _____

9 What / expensive / city / Europe?
   _____

10 Who / friendly / person you know?
   _____

10.3 The Great Outdoors — Survival

VOCABULARY
Phrasal verbs

Complete the leaflet with the phrasal verbs in the box.

> find out   give up   look for   put on   set off   take off

Tips for HIKERS

1 Before you _____, make sure you have everything you need.

2 _____ information about where you are going and places along the way.

3 Pack things so they are easy to find; then you won't need to stop to _____ them.

4 Wear a sweater and a coat. You can always _____ one _____ if you get hot.

5 If it gets really cold, _____ a hat and scarf.

6 When you get tired, try not to _____. It can be difficult to start again!

GRAMMAR
Verb + *to* + infinitive

A Reorder the words to make sentences. Add *to* in the right place.

1 get / married / in / June / hope / They
_____

2 wanted / He / more / about / history / know
_____

3 forget / Don't / Hannah / email
_____

4 for / helping / me / keys / find / Thanks / my
_____

5 Sam / college / trying / work / harder / is / at
_____

B Are the sentences correct or incorrect? Correct the incorrect ones.

1 David never remembers locking the door – I'm surprised we haven't been robbed!
2 What have you decided doing?
3 Tina really needs to buy a new phone.
4 David plans visiting his cousin in Canada next year.
5 She learned reading when she was five years old.
6 I'm sorry, but I'd prefer to stay in a hotel.

PRONUNCIATION
Weak forms: /tuː/ and /tə/

Is *to* pronounced /tuː/ or /tə/ in these sentences? Listen and choose the correct sounds.

1 It's important to prepare before you set off.   /tuː/   /tə/
2 Let's try to agree on a hostel.   /tuː/   /tə/
3 Try to believe that you can do it.   /tuː/   /tə/
4 Take some thick socks to put on when you get cold.   /tuː/   /tə/
5 Be careful when you try to open your backpack.   /tuː/   /tə/
6 Make sure you tell someone when you expect to arrive.   /tuː/   /tə/

60 THE GREAT OUTDOORS

10.4 The Great Outdoors — Reading

READING

A PREDICT Look at the pictures. What do you think the article is about?

B READ FOR GIST Read *For the fun of it* and check your ideas from Exercise A.

FOR THE FUN OF IT

LEO SAUNDERS | November 25, 2018 | 1289 COMMENTS

I love traveling – I even earn money writing about it for this magazine. I know most people say they enjoy traveling, but usually what they mean is spending time at their destination. For me it's getting there that is the most exciting part! I'm not interested in when, but how I get somewhere. My best trip this year was biking across the US along the most famous road in the world – Route 66. It's busy and dangerous, especially on a bike, but that's part of the fun. I could only travel about 80 miles a day, which wasn't a bad thing as it gave me time to look around and chat to some of the most interesting people I've ever met. Some of my new friends' stories were amazing. I went in September and I believe that is the best time to go if you're thinking about taking the same trip. It isn't too hot or cold along the route. The hottest part was in New Mexico where it was sunny every day. The whole trip took me just over a month to travel the 2400 miles from Los Angeles to Chicago, and it was amazing. Next year I plan to go along the Danube River in Europe by canoe!

Glossary

route (n) the road or path you use when you go from one place to another

C READ FOR DETAIL Read the article again and answer the questions.

1 Why does Leo think he's different from other travelers?
 a He gets paid to write about traveling.
 b He prefers the journey to the destination.
 c He knows a lot of people who travel.

2 What doesn't interest Leo when he's traveling?
 a Making new friends.
 b Listening to people's stories.
 c Getting somewhere quickly.

3 Why is it an advantage to travel slowly?
 a It gives you time to see things.
 b You don't worry about when you will arrive.
 c You don't need to talk to people you meet.

4 What does Leo recommend his readers to do?
 a Visit New Mexico.
 b Try new experiences.
 c Do the journey in September.

D IDENTIFY FACT AND OPINION Read the article again. Are these facts (F) or opinions (O)?

1 Most people enjoy traveling. ___
2 Leo is paid for writing about traveling. ___
3 Route 66 is in the US. ___
4 Biking on busy roads is often dangerous. ___
5 Leo biked about 80 miles a day. ___
6 September is the best time to travel along Route 66. ___
7 Route 66 is 2400 miles long. ___

E REFLECT Answer the questions.

1 Do you like traveling like Leo or is traveling just a way of getting somewhere?
2 What was the last journey you took? Where did you go? How did you travel?
3 Is there a place you would like to visit or travel to? Where is it? Why do you want to go there?

10.5 The Great Outdoors
Listening; Functional Language

LISTENING

A **LISTEN FOR GIST** Listen to a review. Which picture (1–2) matches the story?

Glossary
connect (v) to join two things together
remote (adj) not near a town or place where there are lots of people
spoiler (n) information about what happens in a story that you may not want to know about before reading a book, seeing a movie, etc for yourself

B **LISTEN FOR DETAIL** Listen again and check (✓) the topics that are discussed.

a How they got to South America ☐
b The location ☐
c The weather ☐
d What happened in the end ☐
e When it happened ☐

C **LISTEN FOR SPECIFIC INFORMATION** Listen again. Complete the sentences with no more than three words from the review.

1 It is an _____ movie.
2 It is the _____ of what happened to two friends.
3 They were climbing in a _____ of the Andes.
4 They tried to climb faster because _____ was bad.
5 On the way down, Joel Sampson fell and _____.
6 There is a second _____ and Steven cuts the rope.
7 Joel Sampson survives and tries to get back to _____.
8 After _____, he reaches the camp and both men are alive.

D **REFLECT** Answer the questions.

1 What did you think of the story?
2 How do you think Joel Sampson survived?
3 Do you know any other stories of survival?

FUNCTIONAL LANGUAGE
Making and responding to invitations

Complete conversations (a–d) with the words and phrases in the box. Then listen and check.

| come | free on | having | I'd love to |
| I'm away | sounds | to come | would be great |

1
Vicky: Do you want to go and see that movie about the two mountaineers, Joel Sampson and Steven Gates, on Saturday? It's a true story and sounds amazing!
Sara: I'm sorry. ¹_____ this weekend.

2
Louise: Are you ²_____ Thursday evening? We're going out to eat.
Dan: ³_____, but I'm working.

3
Rob: We're ⁴_____ a party tomorrow. Can you ⁵_____?
Amy: Yes, that ⁶_____ great.

4
Pavel: Would you like ⁷_____ camping with me next month?
Mark: That ⁸_____.

62 THE GREAT OUTDOORS

10.6 The Great Outdoors — Write a product review

WRITING

A Label the picture with the items in the box.

> a backpack   a camping stove
> a first aid kit   a pair of walking boots

B Read the review page. Match reviews (a–c) with pictures (1–4). There is one extra picture.

C Complete the reviews with the adverb form of the adjectives in the box.

> careful   easy   good   quick   ~~unfortunate~~

a I bought these to use when I go hiking. I had a pair, but they were very old. [1] _Unfortunately_, these ones don't keep your feet dry. They are also difficult to put on. I need to buy a new pair that I can put on [2] _____.

b I got this for when I go camping. You need to use it [3] _____ and it works really [4] _____ for boiling water, but not for anything else. Next time I think I'll buy a more expensive model.

c My father bought this for me as a present. I had one before, but this one is bigger and lighter. It has lots of special parts so I can find things [5] _____. I love it.

D Read the reviews again. Write notes about each using the table below.

	Review a	Review b	Review c
What is the product?			
What are its bad points?			
What are its good points?			
Would the reviewer recommend it?			

WRITING PRACTICE

A PREPARE You are going to write a review for a product you recently bought. Use the questions in Exercise D to help you write notes.

B WRITE Use your notes and some adverbs to write your review. Remember to use adverbs of manner.

THE GREAT OUTDOORS 63

11.1 The Body — Health tips

VOCABULARY
The body

Label body parts (1–10) with the words in the box.

| arm | brain | ear | eye | foot | hand | heart |
| leg | neck | nose |

1 _____

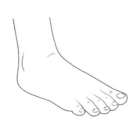
2 _____

3 _____

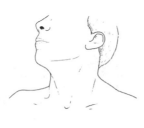
4 _____

5 _____

6 _____

7 _____

8 _____

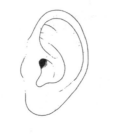
9 _____   10 _____

GRAMMAR
should and shouldn't

A Correct the mistakes in each sentence.

1 We should go to the beach today or tomorrow?
2 A: I should buy John a birthday present.
  B: No, you should. He didn't buy you one.
3 We're going on vacation in August so the weather should sunny.
4 They shouldn't to talk to their mom like that.

B Give advice using *should* or *shouldn't* for the following situations.

1 Rachel always feels tired in the morning. (*don't go to bed late*)
   You shouldn't go to bed late.
2 Lucy always feels sick after eating nuts. (*don't eat nuts*)
   You _____.
3 Brad hasn't studied for his exam next week. (*study now*)
   You _____.
4 Your friend works too hard. (*relax more*)
   You _____.
5 Your friend always drives everywhere he goes. (*walk sometimes*)
   You _____.

PRONUNCIATION
Sentence stress

🔊 Listen and repeat the sentences. Underline *should* or
11.1 *shouldn't* if it is stressed.

1 You should try to eat lots of fruits and vegetables.
2 You shouldn't drink too much tea.
3 You should get plenty of exercise.
4 You shouldn't worry about it too much.
5 You should exercise your brain every day.

64 THE BODY

11.2 The Body — In it to win it

GRAMMAR
Present perfect

A Use the prompts to write present perfect sentences or questions.

1 you / meet / famous person?
   Have you ever met a famous person?

2 you / ride / elephant?
   _____

3 I / not go / Japan
   _____

4 she / write / ten books
   _____

5 I / not live / abroad
   _____

6 you / run / marathon?
   _____

B Look at Roberto's and Lucy's Bucket Lists (the things they want to do before they die). Complete the sentences using the present perfect.

Lucy's Bucket List	Roberto's Bucket List
swim with dolphins [✓]	buy a house [✗]
climb Kilimanjaro [✗]	go to New York [✓]
eat octopus [✓]	eat octopus [✓]
fly a plane [✓]	take a photo on the Great Wall of China [✗]
win the lottery [✗]	win the lottery [✗]

1 Lucy ___*has swum*___ with dolphins.
2 Roberto _____ a house.
3 Lucy _____ Kilimanjaro.
4 Roberto _____ to New York.
5 They _____ octopus.
6 Lucy _____ a plane.
7 Roberto _____ on the Great Wall of China.
8 They _____ the lottery.

VOCABULARY
Irregular past participles

Choose the correct past participles (a, b or c) to complete the sentences.

1 Ben's not here today. He's … on vacation.
   a been   **b** gone   **c** taken

2 Libby's favorite soccer team haven't … a game this year.
   a finished   **b** done   **c** won

3 I've never … a camel before. This will be the first time.
   a gone   **b** ridden   **c** taken

4 Greg is very careless. He's … his leg again!
   a broken   **b** done   **c** eaten

5 I've … too much. I have a stomach ache.
   a done   **b** eaten   **c** seen

6 Come on! I'm sure you've … enough photos.
   a had   **b** done   **c** taken

7 Oh no! I've … to bring any money! Can you pay for me?
   a forgotten   **b** remembered   **c** had

8 Don't worry. I've never … any sharks here and I come to this beach every year.
   a ridden   **b** eaten   **c** seen

PRONUNCIATION
Past participles

🔊 11.2 Listen and ⃝circle the past participle that has a different sound.

1 done   forgotten   run
2 eaten   forgotten   won
3 gone   ridden   taken
4 been   ridden   seen
5 won   broken   eaten

THE BODY   65

11.3 The Body Move it

GRAMMAR
Present perfect vs simple past

A Choose the correct options to complete the sentences.

1. **I've played / I played** soccer with some of my friends from work last night.
2. It says here that **he joined / he's joined** the company five years ago.
3. **We went / We've been** to an amazing Japanese restaurant for dinner on the weekend.
4. I went to Barcelona last year, but I **never went / 've never been** to Madrid.
5. The weather was terrible yesterday. It **'s rained / rained** all day.
6. I love running marathons. I **did / 've done** three already this year.

B Complete the sentences with the present perfect or simple past form of the verbs in parentheses.

1. I _____ (go) to Istanbul for a conference last week.
2. He _____ (climb) two mountains this year.
3. *The Secret History* is my favorite book. I _____ (read) it seven times!
4. We _____ (see) an amazing movie at the movie theater last night!
5. My parents _____ (get married) ten years ago.
6. I _____ (not see) the news today. What's happening?

PRONUNCIATION
Contractions

🔊 Listen and check (✓) the sentences you hear. Then listen
11.3 again and repeat the sentences.

1. ☐ **a** He has been climbing for ten years.
   ☐ **b** He's been climbing for ten years.
2. ☐ **a** He has never been afraid of heights.
   ☐ **b** He's never been afraid of heights.
3. ☐ **a** You have always been adventurous.
   ☐ **b** You've always been adventurous.
4. ☐ **a** I have never had an accident.
   ☐ **b** I've never had an accident.
5. ☐ **a** I've always enjoyed rock climbing.
   ☐ **b** I have always enjoyed rock climbing.

VOCABULARY
Sports

Label pictures (1–10) with *go*, *do* or *play* and a sport.

1 _____

2 _____

3 _____

4 _____

5 _____

6 _____

7 _____

8 _____

9 _____

10 _____

11.4 The Body — Reading

READING

A Look at the picture. What is this activity? Have you ever done it?

B **READ FOR GIST** Read the interview and choose the best summary (1 or 2).

1 Martin wanted a new hobby and has always enjoyed extreme sports, so he decided to try rock climbing.

2 Martin needed to improve his health and didn't want to do typical sports, so he decided to try rock climbing.

Age is just a number

Do you want to do something more exciting? This week, we're talking to Martin Lutt, a rock climber, who is 74!

So when did you start rock climbing?

I've been a climber for about ten years. The first time I tried it was on my birthday. My doctor told me to do more exercise, but I didn't want to play golf or go to the gym so I decided to do something more adventurous.

It's fairly dangerous, were you not worried?

No, not really. I've never been afraid of heights and I have always enjoyed exciting sports, so rock climbing seemed like a good idea. I joined a local club and learned to climb on an indoor wall. I did my first outdoor climb two years ago. It was such a great experience. I've done six more since then, and I still practice on the indoor wall every week.

Have you ever injured yourself?

Yes, I broke a bone in my foot last year. It took a long time to get better, but now I can climb again and I'm planning my next adventure!

Glossary

adventurous (adj) new, unusual and exciting
injure (v) hurt or cause pain

C **READ FOR DETAIL** Read the interview again. Are these sentences true (T) or false (F)? Correct the false sentences.

1 Martin has been a rock climber all his life. *T / F*

2 His wife told him to do more exercise. *T / F*

3 He wasn't interested in playing golf or going to the gym. *T / F*

4 He isn't afraid of heights. *T / F*

5 He wants to continue climbing. *T / F*

D **IDENTIFY THE SEQUENCE OF PAST EVENTS** Read again. Number the events in the order they happened.

___ Martin broke a bone in his foot.

___ The doctor told Martin to do more exercise.

___ Martin did his first outdoor climb.

___ Martin learned to climb on an indoor wall.

___ Martin joined a local club.

E **REFLECT** Answer the questions.

1 Is rock climbing popular in your country?

2 Which new sport would you like to try?

3 Do you prefer team or individual sports? Why?

THE BODY 67

11.5 The Body — Listening; Functional Language

LISTENING

A LISTEN FOR KEY WORDS Listen to a conversation about exercise. Check (✓) the sports that are discussed.

B LISTEN FOR DETAIL Listen again. Choose the correct names to complete the sentences.

1 *Sophie / Hannah* feels tired.
2 *Sophie / Hannah* often goes for a run when she feels tired.
3 *Sophie / Hannah* goes to a yoga class.
4 *Sophie / Hannah* has tried yoga and didn't like it.
5 *Sophie / Hannah* decides to go to a boxing class.
6 *Sophie / Hannah* says it's a good way to protect herself.

C REFLECT Answer the questions.

1 Do you do any of the sports that Sophie and Hannah talk about?
2 What do you think of the different sports?
3 Would you like to join a boxing class? Why/Why not?

FUNCTIONAL LANGUAGE
Asking for information

A Complete the conversation with the words in the box.

> are there   can I   do I   how long
> how much   when

Receptionist: Good afternoon, can I help you?
Sophie: Yes, I'd like some information about your boxing classes.
Receptionist: OK, great. What would you like to know?
Sophie: ¹_____ are the classes?
Receptionist: They're on Tuesdays and Fridays at seven o'clock in the evening.
Sophie: Twice a week ... great. And ²_____ are the classes?
Receptionist: They finish at nine o'clock. So they're two hours.
Sophie: Perfect. That's not too late. ³_____ do they cost?
Receptionist: It's $8 per class or $35 for five classes.
Sophie: Hmm ... I think I'll go for five classes. ⁴_____ need to bring any equipment?
Receptionist: No, just your usual gym clothes. We provide gloves ...
Sophie: Great! ⁵_____ any lockers for our bags?
Receptionist: Yes, they're in the changing rooms. Just bring a lock.
Sophie: OK, I have one at home. ⁶_____ pay for the classes now?
Receptionist: Yes, of course. Please can I have your card number?

B Listen and check your answers to Exercise A.

68 THE BODY

11.6 The Body — Write a recommendation on a forum

WRITING

A Read the post on a health website. What's it about?

> My doctor says I need to lose some weight and try to live a healthy lifestyle. The problem is I don't like sports, I prefer watching TV. I know one thing I should do is eat healthy food, but I love cakes and chocolate too much and I don't want to give them up. Does anyone have any advice?
>
> **Larry** March 7, 3:10 pm

B Read the three recommendations (1–3). Which do you think is the best one? Why?

C Read the recommendations again. Answer these questions.
1. What advice does Jasmine give?
2. What sport does Sammy suggest?
3. What two pieces of advice does Trevor give?

D Complete the recommendations with the adverbs in the box.

> also   as well   too

WRITING PRACTICE

A PREPARE You are going to write a recommendation for Larry. Write notes. Think about why your advice would be good for Larry and what problems there might be.

B WRITE Use your notes to write a recommendation for the forum. Use *also*, *too* and *as well* to add information.

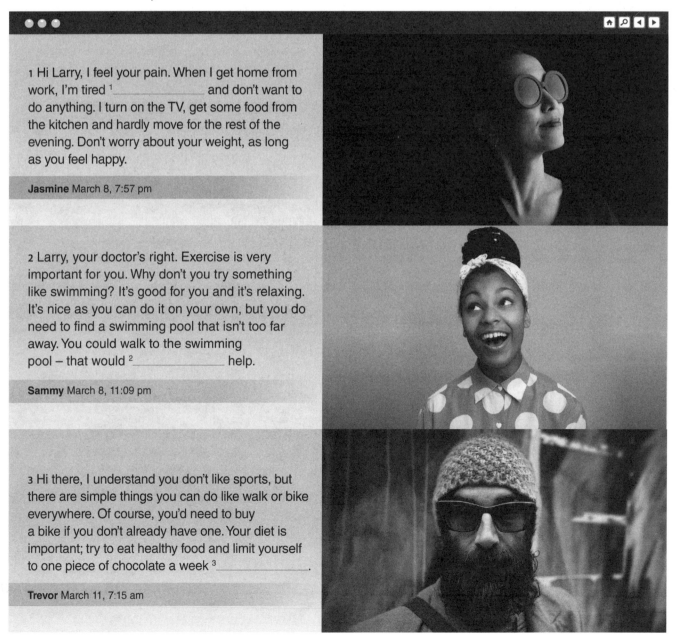

1 Hi Larry, I feel your pain. When I get home from work, I'm tired ¹_____ and don't want to do anything. I turn on the TV, get some food from the kitchen and hardly move for the rest of the evening. Don't worry about your weight, as long as you feel happy.

Jasmine March 8, 7:57 pm

2 Larry, your doctor's right. Exercise is very important for you. Why don't you try something like swimming? It's good for you and it's relaxing. It's nice as you can do it on your own, but you do need to find a swimming pool that isn't too far away. You could walk to the swimming pool – that would ²_____ help.

Sammy March 8, 11:09 pm

3 Hi there, I understand you don't like sports, but there are simple things you can do like walk or bike everywhere. Of course, you'd need to buy a bike if you don't already have one. Your diet is important; try to eat healthy food and limit yourself to one piece of chocolate a week ³_____.

Trevor March 11, 7:15 am

12.1 Modern Lives — Life's too busy

GRAMMAR
going to

A Use the prompts and *going to* to complete the sentences and questions. Use contractions where possible.

1 you / do / tonight / ?
   What are you going to do tonight?

2 I / go / the movie theater / with my friends
   _____

3 Tim / not finish / his essay
   _____

4 How / you / get home / ?
   _____

5 Emma / start college / in September
   _____

6 My mother / not cook / tonight
   _____

7 What / you / have / for lunch / ?
   _____

8 Darren / run / a marathon / this weekend
   _____

B Look at Sophie's weekly planner and complete the short text with *going to* or *not going to*.

Mon:	meet Joe for lunch	✓
Tues:	go to the dentist's	✗
Wed:	visit Mom in the hospital	✓
Thurs:	play tennis with Beth and Amanda	✓
Fri:	buy a new pair of shoes	✗
Sat:	take the children to the park	✓
Sun:	watch Matthew play soccer	✗

Sophie has a busy life. Here is a typical week of hers. On Monday she's ¹_____ meet Joe for lunch and then go shopping. On Tuesday she has an appointment at the dentist's, but she's ²_____ go because she hates the dentist. On Wednesday she's ³_____ visit her mother in hospital. Then on Thursday she's ⁴_____ play tennis with her friends. On Friday she was planning to go shopping to buy new shoes, but now she's ⁵_____ go because she doesn't have enough money. On Saturday she's ⁶_____ take the children to the park, but on Sunday Sophie is ⁷_____ watch Matthew play soccer because she's ⁸_____ stay at home and relax.

PRONUNCIATION
going to: weak and strong to

🔊 Read the sentences and circle /tə/ or /tuː/. Then listen, 12.1 check and repeat.

1 Are you going to watch TV tonight?   /tə/   /tuː/
2 How are you going to eat all of that?   /tə/   /tuː/
3 Sophie is going to meet Joe for lunch.   /tə/   /tuː/
4 I'm not going to ask you again!   /tə/   /tuː/
5 Sophie isn't going to buy a new pair of shoes.   /tə/   /tuː/

VOCABULARY
Future time expressions

Correct the mistakes in these sentences.

1 Do you know what time we're going to arrive next tomorrow?
2 Simon's going to travel to New York on weekend.
3 I'm going to call Giovanni and ask him to soon come over.
4 Are you going to study at the university year next?
5 Megan is going to get married this one summer.
6 They're not going to arrive here until later this tonight.

70 MODERN LIVES

12.2 Modern Lives — Everything will be shiny

GRAMMAR
will for predictions

Read the email from Susie. Complete Amy's reply with *will* and *won't*.

To: Amy.Chen@inbox.org
From: Susie21@media.co.uk
Subject: News!

Hi Amy, I'm really excited as I'm moving to Shanghai next week to start a new job. In fact, it's my first job because I've just graduated from the university where I studied Art and Design. My job is to teach English to young children in a school. I've never taught English before, but I like children. I don't speak Chinese, but I'm going to take lessons. I'm not very good at learning languages and I hope Chinese isn't too difficult. My biggest worry is that I'm vegetarian, I don't eat meat and I'm not very good at cooking. I hope there are good places to eat.

Love, Susie

To: Susie21@media.co.uk
From: Amy.Chen@inbox.org
Subject: Re: News!

Hi Susie, it's great to hear from you. I'm sure you ¹_____ love Shanghai. It's a nice city and you ²_____ find a lot to do there. Here's a photo of my brother and his friends. He went there on vacation last year. I know you ³_____ find life there very different and you ⁴_____ be able to sleep in late. It's going to be very different from when you were a student! I'm sure you ⁵_____ enjoy the job as well. As for learning Chinese, you ⁶_____ find it easy, Chinese is a very difficult language, but I know you ⁷_____ try your best. What about the food? You ⁸_____ definitely find it difficult as a vegetarian, but there are a lot of new restaurants opening so you ⁹_____ have a problem finding a few places to eat. Maybe you ¹⁰_____ learn to cook. ☺

Love, Amy

VOCABULARY
Collocations with *get*

Complete the conversations with the phrases in the box.

> get a coffee   get any sugar   get home   get some cash
> getting married   get some new clothes   got a new job

Sara: Hi Jane! It's good to see you again. Do you want to ¹_____?

Jane: That's a great idea, but I'll need to go and ²_____ out.

Sara: Don't worry! I'll pay for it. I just ³_____.

Jane: Oh, really? Wow! So we have a lot to talk about then!

Sara: Here's your coffee. I didn't ⁴_____ …

Jane: Oh, that's fine, I don't take sugar. So, when do you start your new job?

Sara: Next month. I need to ⁵_____; everyone dresses so well in that office! What about you? Any news?

Jane: Haven't you heard? Steve and I are ⁶_____ …

Sara: Oh wow! That's wonderful news.

Jane: Thanks! Oh! Look at the time …

Sara: What's wrong?

Jane: Nothing, but I promised Steve I'd ⁷_____ by four o'clock.

Sara: OK. Well it was nice to see you again. Bye.

PRONUNCIATION
Contractions: *'ll*

🔊 Listen and check (✓) the sentences you hear. Then listen
12.2 again and repeat the sentences.

1. ☐ **a** You will love it there.
   ☐ **b** You'll love it there.

2. ☐ **a** I'm sure you will enjoy the job.
   ☐ **b** I'm sure you'll enjoy the job.

3. ☐ **a** Susie will find Chinese difficult.
   ☐ **b** Susie'll find Chinese difficult.

4. ☐ **a** We will be able to speak Chinese together.
   ☐ **b** We'll be able to speak Chinese together.

5. ☐ **a** You will find plenty of places to eat.
   ☐ **b** You'll find plenty of places to eat.

MODERN LIVES   71

12.3 Modern Lives — Communication

VOCABULARY
Internet communication

Complete the text with the words in the box.

blog chat connected follow likes
share tweet uploaded

My name is Charlie Reid and I'm a professional photographer. I have a travel ¹_____ where I write about my adventures and ² _____ my photos. Here's one I ³ _____ last week when I was in Antarctica. I can see how many people ⁴ _____ me and one thing that's very interesting is to see the number of ⁵ _____ my photos get. It's amazing how easy it is to stay ⁶ _____ to people around the world. In fact, I use social media to ⁷ _____ with my daughter when I'm away from home. I don't ⁸ _____ yet, but I guess I should.

PRONUNCIATION
Diphthongs

 A Match the words with the same underlined sound. Then
12.3 listen and check.

1 F<u>a</u>cebook   a p<u>o</u>st
2 <u>u</u>sed   b n<u>ow</u>
3 l<u>i</u>ke   c b<u>oo</u>t
4 ch<u>oo</u>se   d enj<u>oy</u>
5 m<u>ou</u>se   e <u>eig</u>ht
6 f<u>o</u>llow   f c<u>u</u>te
7 p<u>oi</u>nt   g tr<u>y</u>

B Listen and circle the word with a different diphthong in
12.4 each group.

1 men<u>u</u>   ch<u>a</u>t   h<u>u</u>man
2 vide<u>o</u>   f<u>o</u>llow   t<u>ou</u>rist
3 bl<u>o</u>g   n<u>oi</u>se   b<u>oy</u>
4 m<u>ou</u>th   n<u>ow</u>   kn<u>ow</u>

GRAMMAR
might

A Complete the conversation with *might* or *might not* and a verb in the box.

be go join leave see stay take

Phil: Hi Lucy. It's Phil.
Lucy: Hi Phil. Where are you?
Phil: I'm on my way, but I ¹_____ a little late. I have to finish this report at work.
Lucy: Oh, OK. How long do you think you'll be?
Phil: I'm not sure. It ² _____ another half an hour or so. Why?
Lucy: Well, we ³ _____ here much longer. We thought we ⁴ _____ soon.
Phil: Really? Where will you go?
Lucy: I'm not too sure. The others are talking about going to another place, but I ⁵ _____ them, I ⁶ _____ home instead.
Phil: Right, well I'll be as quick as I can and I ⁷ _____ you there.
Lucy: OK, I'll text you if we leave.
Phil: Thanks.

B Choose the correct responses (a or b) to the questions.

1 Have you decided what you're doing next year?
   a Yes, I have a job at my dad's company, so I'm going to work there.
   b Yes, I have a job at my dad's company, so I might work there.
2 Do you have any plans for the weekend?
   a I'm not sure. I'm going to meet some friends and go shopping.
   b I'm not sure. I might meet some friends and go shopping.
3 What do you think you'll be doing in ten years' time?
   a That's a difficult question. I'm going to move to Australia.
   b That's a difficult question. I might move to Australia.
4 Are you going on vacation this year?
   a I'm not sure yet. I might go to Spain with some friends in the summer.
   b I'm not sure yet. I'm going to Spain with some friends in the summer.

12.4 Modern Lives — Reading

READING

A PREDICT Look at the title of the blog post and the picture. What do you think the post is about?

B SCAN Read the blog post quickly to check your ideas from Exercise A.

C READ FOR GIST Read the blog post and check (✓) the topics that Mike makes predictions about.

- ☐ cell phones
- ☐ robots
- ☐ photos
- ☐ houses
- ☐ power
- ☐ education
- ☐ battery
- ☐ internet

> **Glossary**
> **communication (n)** talking or writing to give or exchange information
> **expert (n)** someone who has a special skill or knows a lot about something
> **power (n)** the energy that makes something work

D READ FOR DETAIL Read the blog again. Choose the correct options (a, b or c) to complete the sentences.

1. Mike is always surprised at how …
   a easy it is to make predictions.
   b many people follow him on Twitter.
   c many people are interested in his opinions.

2. Mike …
   a has 100,000 followers on Twitter.
   b writes a blog about technology.
   c works for a technology company.

3. Mike says that 15 years ago …
   a the most common use for a cell phone was to call someone.
   b most people didn't have a cell phone.
   c people used their cell phones to do lots of things.

4. Mike says that today people don't often use their cell phones to …
   a pay for things in stores.
   b make calls.
   c connect to the internet.

5. Mike predicts that in the future we'll use cell phones …
   a only when we're at home.
   b to cook our food.
   c that use energy from water.

E REFLECT Answer the questions.

1. What do you use your cell phone for most?
2. Has the way you use your phone changed? If yes, how?
3. Do you use social media like Twitter and Facebook? How?

Calling home
by Mike Samuelson

People often ask me what the next new thing is going to be in the world of communication. I always say that making predictions is not easy, but then I guess as a technology expert it is my job. I now have about 100,000 people who read my blog posts every week and about 3 million followers on Twitter. It always amazes me how many people seem to be interested in what I have to say.

Fifteen years ago most people only used their cell phones to make a phone call, but today we use them to take photos, send messages, go on the internet, pay for things in stores … and we don't make many phone calls! In the next five years the power of our cell phones will increase even more. One thing that might change a lot is the battery. In the future we might have phones that use water for power. I also think we'll use our phones to connect with the things we have at home. So we'll turn the lights on before we get home. We'll send a message to our fridge and we'll have a robot that takes our food out and puts it in the microwave to cook. Next week I'm going to blog about the future of transportation …

12.5 Modern Lives — Listening; Functional Language

LISTENING

A PREPARE You're going to listen to a podcast about the future. Look at pictures (a–c). What do you think the speakers might talk about?

B LISTEN FOR GIST Listen to the podcast. Match speakers (1–3) to pictures (a–c). How many of your predictions in Exercise A did you get right?

> **Glossary**
> **podcast (n)** a radio show you can download and play on a computer, phone or tablet
> **prediction (n)** what you think will happen in the future

C LISTEN FOR DETAIL Listen again. Are these sentences true (T) or false (F)? Correct the false sentences.

1. Tom thinks everyone will drive the same cars as today. T / F
2. He doesn't think we will have jetpacks. T / F
3. When Jenny was young, she had a cell phone. T / F
4. Jenny thinks we'll have robots doing most of the work. T / F
5. Richard doesn't think life will change. T / F
6. Ellen likes the idea of eating food that isn't fresh. T / F

D REFLECT Answer the questions.

1. Do you agree with any of the people? Which one(s)?
2. What are your predictions for the future?

FUNCTIONAL LANGUAGE
Showing interest in something

Complete the conversation with the expressions in the box. 12.6 Then listen and check.

> don't worry   I love it   it doesn't matter
> no problem   that's a shame   that's terrible

Laura: Hi Ellen, I'm sorry I'm late!
Ellen: ¹_____.
Laura: I was going to text, but I realized I'd left my phone at home.
Ellen: ²_____. I just did some shopping.
Laura: I'm always too busy to go shopping. Did you buy anything?
Ellen: Yes, I bought this dress. What do you think?
Laura: ³_____! You'll look amazing in it.
Ellen: Thanks. So do you want to go and get a coffee?
Laura: Sure. Oh no! I've lost my wallet.
Ellen: What? ⁴_____!
Laura: I'm sorry, but I can't go for a coffee now.
Ellen: ⁵_____, but I understand.
Laura: I'm going to see if I left it on the bus.
Ellen: ⁶_____! The most important thing is to find your wallet. Call me later.
Laura: OK, I will. Bye!

12.6 Modern Lives — Write a formal email

WRITING

June 2nd – A day for our son! Hosted by Angus and Julia
The Baytree York, UK.

Come and join us to celebrate our son's graduation. Liam's graduation ceremony will be at 10 am on June 2nd. We are planning a small party for friends and family after the graduation ceremony finishes. We've booked a private room at The Baytree in York and there will be food and drink for 50 guests.

Please send replies to Lara Stevenson as she is organizing everything for us.

A Read the invitation. What's it for?
- a an anniversary
- b a birthday
- c a graduation
- d a wedding

B Put these sentences and phrases in the correct order to make a reply.
- ☐ Also, we will rent a car at the airport. Is there a parking lot at The Baytree where we can leave the car?
- ☐ Can you let us know if there are any rooms at The Baytree, or can you suggest a suitable hotel?
- ☐ Dear Ms. Stevenson,
- ☐ I am writing to you to inform you that we plan to attend Liam's graduation party on June 2nd.
- ☐ Kind regards, Pierre (and Mari) Lefevre
- ☐ We look forward to hearing from you.
- ☐ We will fly over from France on June 1st, so we will need to stay at a hotel in York.

C Read the reply again. Answer these questions.
1. Why are they writing to Ms. Stevenson?
2. Where are the Lefevres traveling from?
3. When will they arrive in the UK?
4. How are they going to travel from the airport?
5. What do they want to know about The Baytree?

WRITING PRACTICE

A Read the invitation. What's it for?

Amy's 21

March 28th – 21!
Hosted by Ed and Mary

Come and join us to celebrate Amy's 21st! Yes, our daughter is 21. It's amazing how quickly they grow up! We have hired a party organizer for this special occasion, so please contact them for any information you might need. We hope to see you all there.

Contact PartyTime at: partytime@mail.com

B PREPARE You are going to write an email asking for information. Think about what you need to know. Write notes.

C WRITE Use your notes to write your formal email.

MODERN LIVES 75

Audio scripts

UNIT 1

Lesson 1.5, Listening, Exercise A
1.4 **M = Mom   Mx = Max**

M: Uh, hello?

Mx: Hi, Mom!

M: Hello?

Mx: Hello? Can you hear me?

M: Oh, hi Max. How are you?

Mx: I'm fine, thanks. How are you?

M: Not too bad. Your father's at the golf club today and your sister's at work, so it's nice and quiet at home. Where are you now?

Mx: I'm in Hanoi in Vietnam.

M: Really? Wow! What's it like there?

Mx: It's really, really hot and raining a lot.

M: Oh. But, you don't have your umbrella! You left it here.

Mx: Don't worry, Mom. I'm fine. I have a coat.

M: Oh, OK. Well, I hope you're eating well.

Mx: Of course I am.

M: Is the food good?

Mx: Yes, it's delicious.

M: Well, don't eat anything strange out there.

Mx: Ha ha! Strange? Like what?

M: Like . . . like . . . I don't know, insects or something!

Mx: Insects? Well some people do eat grasshoppers . . .

M: Grasshoppers? Max, you must come home!

Mx: Mom, relax. I'm fine. The food's fine. Everything is fine.

M: Hmm . . . OK. Well, what's your next destination?

Mx: Thailand, I think.

M: Do you need any money?

Mx: No, Mom. I have money. Say *Hi* to Dad for me.

M: OK. Bye, darling. Bye. I love you! Remember to . . . Max? Max?

Lesson 1.5, Functional Language
1.5 **Mx = Max   E = Emily**

Mx: Excuse me, is this the train to Sapa?

E: Yes, it is.

Mx: Oh, great. Thanks. I'm Max by the way.

E: Nice to meet you Max. I'm Emily and this is my friend Sophie.

Mx: Nice to meet you both. How are you?

E: Not too bad. And you?

Mx: I'm fine, thanks.

E: So where are you from, Max?

UNIT 2

Lesson 2.5, Listening, Exercise A
2.4 **M = Maha   J = Jess**

J: Hi Maha, sorry I'm late – I had to finish something at work.

M: Ha ha! Don't worry, you're here now. Sit down and relax.

J: All right. How are you, anyway? How was the wedding?

M: It was great. Would you like to see some photos?

J: Sure.

M: OK, hold on . . . Here you go. Here's a picture of the whole family.

J: Oh, wow! There's a lot of you. So, who's who?

M: The young man with the short dark hair is my brother, Hamad.

J: He looks very serious.

M: Ha ha! No, he's not. He's really funny and he makes everyone laugh.

J: And who's the slim woman with long black hair?

M: Do you mean the woman next to him?

J: Yes. Is that his wife?

M: No, that's our cousin, Fauzia.

J: And are those your parents?

M: Yes, my mother is the one with short gray hair and glasses and my father has a beard and a mustache.

J: Everyone looks so happy.

M: Of course! It's a wedding photo.

J: Oh, who's the woman with long blond hair and blue eyes?

M: Oh, that's Mandy. She's my brother's wife. She's American.

J: Well, it looks like an amazing day.

M: Yeah, it was great. Anyway, what do you want to drink?

J: Just a coffee, please. Milk, no sugar.

M: OK, I'll go and order for us.

Lesson 2.5, Functional Language
2.5 **M = Maha   D = Doug**

D: Can I help you?

M: Yes, please. Could I have a coffee with milk and a green tea?

D: Of course. Anything to eat?

M: Could I have a chocolate cookie?

D: No, sorry. I'm afraid not. We don't have any left.

M: OK, no problem. How much is that?

D: That's $4.60.

M: Thanks.

UNIT 3

Lesson 3.5, Listening, Exercise A
3.5 **S = Simon   B = Beth**

S: Hey, Beth – your birthday's this month, isn't it?

B: Ugh! Yes. It's on Saturday.

S: Ha ha! You don't sound very happy about it!

B: I'm old Simon!

76   AUDIO SCRIPTS

Audioscripts

S: What? You're 26! That's not old! Come on, let's do something to celebrate!

B: Why? It's not a special day.

S: Of course it's a special day! It's your birthday. We need to do something ...

B: OK, OK. What do you want to do?

S: Let's have a party!

B: No, I don't want a party. I don't like big groups of people.

S: OK, but we have to celebrate. Why don't we go out to eat?

B: I'm not sure. I don't have a lot of money. Why don't we just cook something here?

S: No. It's a special occasion, so we need to do something special. How about going to see that new Tom Hanks movie?

B: Now, that's a great idea! I love Tom Hanks! What about Friday evening after work?

S: That sounds good. Hold on. Let me check what time it's showing. OK, there are two shows – one at 7:15 and one at 9:30.

B: 9:30 is too late. Let's go to the one at 7:15.

S: Awesome! I'll book the tickets for 7:15.

UNIT 4

🔊 **Lesson 4.5, Listening, Exercise A**
4.4 I = Interviewer   G = Graham

I: Good morning. Can I ask you a few questions about your job?

G: OK, sure.

I: What do you do?

G: I'm an actor! Ha ha!

I: Really? Wow! Do you work on TV?

G: Um, not TV, no.

I: Oh, so movies then? Or the theater?

G: No, not movies or the theater.

I: But I thought you said you're an actor!

G: Well, I want to be an actor.

I: Oh, I see. So what do you do at the moment?

G: I work as a receptionist.

I: Oh! I see. Do you work in an office?

G: Yes, I do. My job is to answer the phones, take messages and greet visitors.

I: Do you work nine to five?

G: Yes, I do and I have an hour for lunch at noon.

I: Do you have to wear a uniform?

G: No, I don't.

I: And do you work for a big company?

G: Yes, it's a very big company. It has offices in 20 different countries.

I: Do you like your job?

G: No, I don't. It's really boring.

I: Do you want to change your job?

G: Not really. I want to move to the Los Angeles office.

I: Oh, to be near Hollywood ...

G: Yes, I want to be a famous Hollywood actor.

I: Thank you, Graham. Next week ...

🔊 **Lesson 4.5, Functional Language**
4.5 R = Receptionist   RK = Richard Kershaw

R: Good morning. This is Schmidt and Brandt. Can I help you?

RK: Hello. Could I speak to Hannah Schmidt, please?

R: Who's speaking, please?

RK: It's Richard Kershaw.

R: Hold on a minute, please. I'm afraid she isn't available right now. Would you like to leave a message?

RK: Yes, please. Can you ask her to call Richard from S-REK Ltd at 800-555-0199, please?

R: I'm sorry, can you repeat that?

UNIT 5

🔊 **Lesson 5.5, Listening, Exercise A**
5.4 V = Victor   H = Hannah

V: So where do you live, Hannah?

H: I live in Camden in north London.

V: Oh, hold on. Is there a really big market there?

H: Yes, that's right. It's amazing!

V: What sort of things can you buy there?

H: Anything, really. Clothes, food, jewelry ... Yes, Camden is a fashionable place to live. There are a few amazing restaurants and some really good cafés.

V: Sounds great.

H: Yeah, some of the restaurants there are amazing, and most of the cafés are pretty good.

V: Is it busy?

H: Uh, yes. It gets really busy on the weekend because it's so popular with tourists. Apparently, around 100,000 people visit Camden every weekend!

V: Wow! Yeah, that is busy. Maybe I should go on Friday. I need to buy a few presents before I fly back on Sunday. Is it close to the station?

H: Yes, it's really easy. Just turn right out of the subway and walk straight up Camden High Street. The market is about a two-minute walk away. I'd go early though, as it gets really, really busy by lunchtime. Anyway, tell me about you. Where do you live?

V: I live in Montreal.

H: In Canada?

V: Yes, that's right. I work at a university there.

H: What's Montreal like?

V: I love it. I live in the center, but my apartment is right next to a park, so it doesn't feel like you're in a really big city.

H: Nice. So is it an interesting place to live?

V: Uh, yes. I think so. There are lots of museums and theaters.

AUDIO SCRIPTS   77

Audio scripts

It is definitely not a boring place to live!

H: Is there anything strange in Montreal?

V: Strange? Well, there's a lot of graffiti and street art which some people don't like, but I think it's great.

H: Ha ha. What about the buildings. Are they all modern?

V: No, there are some beautiful old buildings. To be honest, the only real problem with the city is that it's so popular with tourists. It can get pretty noisy and crowded, especially on the weekend.

H: So Camden and Montreal are very similar . . .

V: Ha ha! Yeah, it sounds like it!

Lesson 5.5, Functional Language, Exercise C
5.5 V = Victor   H = Hannah

V: Hi Hannah. I'm at the subway station.

H: Oh, hey Victor! Do you need directions to my apartment?

V: Yes, please.

H: OK. Come out of the subway station. There is a bank across from the entrance.

V: . . . across from the subway station.

H: Cross over the road and turn left. Then take the first turn on the right.

V: First turn on the right . . .

H: Walk past the movie theater. It's on the left.

V: Movie theater on the right . . .

H: No, on the left. Walk to the end of the road. My apartment is on the left next to the café.

UNIT 6

Lesson 6.5, Listening, Exercise A
6.4 R = Rick   L = Luke   S = Silvia

L: So what did you think of the movie?

S: Honestly, Luke. It wasn't great.

L: Really? I loved it! I thought the actors were great.

S: What do you mean? I thought they were awful.

L: That's not true. How about you, Rick?

R: I'm not sure.

L: What? Come on. The special effects were awesome!

R: Yes, that's true, but you also need good actors and an interesting story.

L: I loved the actors. Meryl Adams was great as the mother.

S: That's true, but the other actors were terrible.

L: Rick, what do you think?

R: Uh, some of the acting was OK, but generally I think I agree with Silvia . . . and the music was awful.

L: What? I love that type of music.

R: I know you do, but I hate it.

L: What about the director? He's amazing.

R: Hmm . . . I don't know. He hasn't won an Oscar, has he?

L: No, that's true but he could win one for this movie.

S: Ha ha! Now I know you're joking!

UNIT 7

Lesson 7.5, Listening, Exercise A
7.4 P = Presenter   T = Tom

P: Joining us now to talk about his latest TV show is the British explorer, Tom Kingsley. Tom, welcome to the show.

T: Thanks for having me.

P: So, Tom – in the show you attempt to travel around the world without flying. Can you tell us a little about your experience?

T: Sure. So I left London and went by train to Paris. From there I took a bus that went through six countries in Europe before I arrived in Athens, Greece. Next, I went by boat to Egypt. After arriving and doing some sightseeing, I rented a car and I drove all the way to Kenya, though I had to go by ferry to cross into Sudan. In Nairobi I found a ship that could take me to India. In Mumbai I bought a motorcycle and rode from India, across South-East Asia all the way to Singapore. I spent a month there before I found another boat that could take me all the way to the US. It took three weeks to arrive! Finally, I took the bus and train across the US.

P: Wow! That sounds like an amazing journey.

T: It really was. It was pretty difficult at times, but I met a lot of amazing people and stayed in some very unusual places.

P: I'm sure you did. Were there any surprises?

T: Well, to be honest, the most difficult part was checking into my first hotel in the US. After traveling so far and staying in so many unusual places, it was kind of strange to be somewhere so normal again!

Lesson 7.5, Functional Language
7.5 R = Receptionist   T = Tom

R: Good afternoon, sir. How can I help you?

T: I have a reservation for a double room for two nights.

R: OK, great. Could I have your passport, please?

T: Of course. Here you are. What time is checkout on Sunday?

R: It's at noon, sir.

T: Great, and is breakfast included?

R: Yes, it is. It's between 6:30 and 10 am in the dining room. Do you need any help with your bags?

T: No, I'm fine thank you. Is there wi-fi in the rooms?

R: Yes, there is. The password is on the desk in your room.

T: OK, great. Thank you.

R: You're welcome, sir. Do you need anything else?

T: Uh . . . yes. Can I have my key?

UNIT 8

Lesson 8.5, Listening, Exercise A
8.4 O = Oli   T = Tara

O: So what's your favorite food, Tara? Sushi? Pasta?

T: Actually, I love American food.

O: Really! What? Like hot dogs and burgers?

78   AUDIO SCRIPTS

Audioscripts

T: Mmmm . . . yes, they're delicious, especially when you cook them on a barbecue!

O: Yes, but that kind of food is so unhealthy!

T: I know, I know . . . but I don't eat it very often. Actually, during the week, I usually eat something simple like salad, or pasta. Anyway, what about you? What's your favorite food?

O: Uh, it's difficult to choose, but Thai food is probably my favorite.

T: Oh, really? Isn't it really hot and spicy?

O: Uh, a lot of the dishes are, yes. But my favorite is made with coconut milk, so it isn't spicy at all. I usually make it with noodles and lots of vegetables . . .

T: No, stop – you're making me hungry!

O: Ha ha! Sorry. Should we go and get some lunch?

T: Yes, please. I'm starving! Why don't we go and have some Italian food?

O: But I thought you like American food?

T: I do, but there's a really good pizza place near here. The slices are enormous!

O: Sounds great, let's go!

Lesson 8.5, Functional Language, Exercise B
8.5 W = Waiter   T = Tara

W: Are you ready to order?

T: Yes, I'll have the chicken salad, please.

W: OK. Would you like something to drink?

T: Could I have a mango juice with ice?

W: Certainly.

W: Would you like to see the dessert menu?

T: No, thanks. Can I have the bill, please?

UNIT 9

Lesson 9.5, Listening, Exercise A
9.4

1 We are a new store opening soon in the shopping center. We offer designer brands at low prices. Max Out is perfect for all those people looking for a bargain.

2 JCs – the local family store with really friendly staff. Come in and talk to us and we'll help you find what you are looking for. There are lots of new items each week, so why not visit and see what we have in stock?

3 Why wait for the sales? At Bargains 2day we have something for everyone. The price is low, but the quality is high.

4 Looking for something special to wear on the weekend? At Tuffin, we only sell quality clothing. Yes, our prices are expensive, but we believe you get what you pay for.

5 TieUp is a great place to shop for all those little things. We sell ties, scarves, gloves and sunglasses at a discount. For all those small things in your wardrobe, TieUp is the place to look.

Lesson 9.5, Functional Language
9.5 S = Store clerk   C = Customer

S: Good morning. Can I help you?

C: No, I'm just looking, thank you. Oh! Actually, can I try these jeans on, please?

S: Of course, the changing rooms are over there.

S: Oh! They look really great on you . . .

C: Thank you, but I think they are a little small. Do you have the same style in medium?

S: Yeah, here you are.

C: These are perfect. How much are they?

S: They're $35, but there's a 10% discount.

C: Oh, great! I'll take them.

UNIT 10

Lesson 10.5, Listening, Exercise A
10.4

YouTuber: Hello YouTube, and welcome to another episode of *Lost the plot*. Each week I tell you the plot of a new movie in just one minute. Oh, and remember, there will be spoilers! This week I'm talking about Wes Carpenter's new adventure movie *A Long Way Down*.

It tells the true story of two friends, Joel Sampson and Steven Gates, who try to climb to the top of a mountain in a remote part of the Andes in South America. The two friends reach the top of the mountain, but on their way down, the weather becomes really bad and they try to climb faster. Unfortunately, Joel falls on the way down and breaks his leg. The two friends carry on trying to get to the bottom of the mountain, but the situation gets worse. Then another accident happens and, in the end, Steven cuts the rope that connects the two men together. Joel falls again, but somehow he survives. When he finds out he is alone on the mountain, he tries to get back to their camp. It takes him three days, but finally he makes it. Amazingly, the two men both live to tell the story.

Lesson 10.5, Functional Language
10.5 V = Vicky   S = Sara   L = Louise
D = Dan   R = Rob   A = Amy
P = Pavel   M = Mark

1

V: Do you want to go and see that movie about the two mountaineers, Joel Sampson and Steven Gates, on Saturday? It's a true story and sounds amazing!

S: I'm sorry. I'm away this weekend.

2

L: Are you free on Thursday evening? We're going out for a meal.

D: I'd love to, but I'm working.

3

R: We're having a party tomorrow. Can you come?

A: Yes, that sounds great.

4

P: Would you like to come camping with me next month?

M: That would be great.

AUDIO SCRIPTS   79

Audio scripts

UNIT 11

🔊 **Lesson 11.5, Listening, Exercise A**
11.4 **S = Sophie   H = Hannah**

S: I feel so tired.

H: What you need is exercise, Sophie.

S: Exercise? How will that make me less tired?

H: You'd be surprised. When I feel tired, I go for a swim or a run and I always feel better afterward.

S: Hmm . . . I might have to give it a try.

H: You could come with me when I go to my next yoga class.

S: No, thanks. I've tried yoga and I didn't enjoy it.

H: Well, there are lots of other sports you could do. Let me show you the local health club's website. Hmm . . . Here you go.

S: Oh, look. They have boxing classes.

H: Boxing! Are you crazy?

S: No, why shouldn't I learn to box?

H: Well, I guess you'll get fit . . .

S: Yes, and learn to protect myself.

H: Let me know how it goes. I might join you at the classes.

🔊 **Lesson 11.5, Functional Language, Exercise B**
11.5 **R = Receptionist   S = Sophie**

R: Good afternoon, can I help you?

S: Yes, I'd like some information about your boxing classes.

R: OK, great! What would you like to know?

S: When are the classes?

R: They're on Tuesdays and Fridays at seven o'clock in the evening.

S: Twice a week . . . great and how long are the classes?

R: They finish at nine o'clock. So they're two hours.

S: Perfect. That's not too late. How much do they cost?

R: It's $8 per class or $35 for five classes.

S: Hmm . . . I think I'll go for five classes. Do I need to bring any equipment?

R: No, just your usual gym clothes. We provide gloves.

S: Great! Are there any lockers for our bags?

R: Yes, they're in the changing rooms. Just bring a lock.

S: OK, I have one at home. Can I pay for the classes now?

R: Yes, of course. Please can I have your card number?

UNIT 12

🔊 **Lesson 12.5, Listening, Exercise B**
12.5 **E = Ellen   T = Tom   J = Jenny   R = Richard**

1

E: Hello and welcome to The Lowdown. I'm your host Ellen Michaels and on today's show we're talking to people on the street about their predictions for the future. Hi, what's your name?

T: Hi I'm Tom! I'm 22 and I'm a student.

E: So Tom, how do you think life will change in the next 20 years?

T: Wow! That's a big question. Well, I don't think we'll be driving around in cars . . .

E: Ha ha ha. Do you think we'll have jetpacks?

T: Um, no. I think we'll have flying cars.

2

E: Excuse me, can I ask you a few questions?

J: Sure.

E: So, first of all. What's your name and how old are you?

J: I'm Jenny and I'm 56.

E: So you must have seen a lot of changes over the years. How do you think life will change in the next 20 years?

J: That's a difficult question. When I was young, there were no cell phones and look at today. I think one change is that we'll have robots doing most of the jobs.

3

R: Hi, I'm Richard and I'm a retired firefighter from New York.

E: How do you think life will change over the next 20 years?

R: Well, I don't really know to be honest . . . Maybe we'll all eat food that comes in packages . . .

E: You mean we won't have fresh food?

R: Yes, exactly. I know it's a shame, but I think that's what will happen.

E: Yuck!

🔊 **Lesson 12.5, Functional Language**
12.6 **L = Laura   E = Ellen**

L: Hi Ellen, I'm sorry I'm late!

E: Don't worry!

L: I was going to text, but I realized I'd left my phone at home.

E: It doesn't matter. I just did some shopping.

L: I'm always too busy to go shopping. Did you buy anything?

E: Yes, I bought this dress. What do you think?

L: I love it! You'll look amazing in it.

E: Thanks. So do you want to go and get a coffee?

L: Sure. Oh no! I've lost my wallet.

E: What? That's terrible!

L: I'm sorry, but I can't go for a coffee now.

E: That's a shame, but I understand.

L: I'm going to see if I left it on the bus.

E: No problem! The most important thing is to find your wallet. Call me later.

L: OK, I will. Bye!

Answer key

1.1 People and places
VOCABULARY

A

1 Canada **2** US **3** Mexico **4** Brazil **5** Spain **6** France
7 Turkey **8** India **9** China **10** Japan

B

1 Canada **2** Canadian **3** Japanese **4** Mexico
5 Mexican **6** Chinese **7** China **8** British
9 Sweden **10** Swedish

PRONUNCIATION

●●	●●	●●●	●●●	●●●●
British Polish	Brazil Japan	Mexican	Japanese Vietnam	Canadian Colombia

GRAMMAR

A

1 'm **2** 're **3** is **4** 'm not **5** aren't **6** isn't

B

1 'm/am **2** is **3** 'm/am **4** isn't / is not **5** 's / is
6 're / are **7** is **8** 're / are **9** aren't / are not **10** 're / are
11 's / is **12** 'm / am **13** 'm not / am not **14** 'm / am
15 're / are

1.2 Where are you?
VOCABULARY

A

2 25,312 **3** 9,730 **4** 2,500,000 **5** 18,880 **6** 316

B

1 e **2** b **3** d **4** a **5** c

PRONUNCIATION

1 30 **2** 14 **3** 60 **4** 15 **5** 13 **6** 18

GRAMMAR

A

2 Tell me about the city. ~~It is~~ **Is it** expensive?
3 ~~Is~~ **Are** your parents Japanese?
4 Hi, Erin! How **are you**?
5 **Is it** hot there?
6 What's your favorite type of food?
7 Oh, really? Where **are you** now?
8 **Are you** ~~is~~ busy?

B

2 Are you Spanish?
3 How far is Seoul from Paris?
4 Where are you now?
5 What's your favorite food?

1.3 What's in your bag?
VOCABULARY

1 headphones **5** watch **9** magazine
2 umbrella **6** wallet **10** cell phone
3 money **7** tissues **11** bottle of water
4 laptop **8** keys **12** credit card

GRAMMAR

A

1 an **2** an **3** a **4** – **5** an **6** a **7** – **8** a

B

1 that **2** those **3** this **4** these **5** these **6** that

PRONUNCIATION

2 book **3** wallet **4** it **5** watch **6** tissues

1.4 Reading
READING

A

1 Elsa **2** Sandra **3** Ralph **4** Greg

B

1 cold **2** headphones **3** credit card **4** work **5** baby
6 a newspaper **7** everything **8** have food

1.5 Listening; Functional Language
LISTENING

A

1 a **2** b **3** c **4** c

B

1 T
2 F (It's really, really hot and raining a lot.)
3 F (Max says it's delicious.)
4 T
5 T
6 F (He says he has money.)

FUNCTIONAL LANGUAGE

1 I'm **2** meet **3** this **4** How **5** too **6** fine

1.6 Fill in a form with personal details
WRITING

A

1 c **2** b **3** a

B

1 First **2** Last **3** Home **4** Phone **5** Email
6 Occupation **7** Type **8** Number **9** Payment
10 Duration

C

1 Jemma **2** Khan **3** Chinese **4** Shanghai **5** China

WRITING PRACTICE

Model answer

Registration form for English classes.	
First name: Julian	**Nationality:** French
Last name: Duchamp	**Email:** jd123@languageschool.fr
Date of birth: 12/08/1994	**Phone number:** 555 124552
Duration of course: 3 weeks ☐ 6 weeks ☐ 12 weeks ☑	
Payment type: Cash ☐ Debit card ☑ Credit card ☐	

ANSWER KEY 81

Answer key

2.1 Family
VOCABULARY
2 mother **3** husband **4** grandmother **5** uncle
6 cousins **7** grandfather **8** parents **9** sister **10** wife
11 aunt **12** children **13** father

PRONUNCIATION
1 cousin **2** famous **3** husband **4** curious **5** actress
6 celebrate **7** family **8** again

GRAMMAR
A

1 my **2** her **3** our **4** Their **5** His **6** Its

B

1 parents' **2** sister's **3** wife's **4** grandparents'
5 children's **6** David's **7** James's **8** weeks'

2.2 The same, but different
VOCABULARY
A

1 d **2** c **3** e **4** f **5** a **6** b

B

Hair length	Hair type	Hair color	Other
long	bald	blond	beard
short	curly	brown	glasses
	straight	gray	mustache

GRAMMAR
A

1 have **2** Does **3** has **4** don't have
5 have **6** doesn't have **7** Does **8** have

B

1 My uncle has a Ferrari.
2 Amy and Tim don't have any children.
3 Does your mother have blue eyes?
4 He doesn't have a famous cousin.
5 Both of my sisters have blond hair.
6 Danielle's sister doesn't have her sunglasses today.
7 I have a car, but my brother doesn't.
8 We don't have time to go to the store.

PRONUNCIATION
1 She has **2** We have **3** I have **4** She has
5 he has **6** you have **7** She has **8** we have

2.3 Friends
VOCABULARY
A

1 messy **2** noisy **3** serious **4** friendly **5** quiet

B

1 c **2** a **3** a **4** c **5** b **6** c **7** c

PRONUNCIATION

●	●●	●●●	●●●
blond	curly	serious	unfriendly
neat	different		unhappy
straight	quiet		
tall			

GRAMMAR
A

1 Tristan is a fairly serious person.
2 Your roommates are very friendly.
3 My sister's bedroom is really messy.
4 Are your neighbors very noisy?
5 The office is very quiet this morning.
6 Is your new apartment expensive?

B

1 My boss isn't a very friend**ly** person. He is always shouting.
2 What happened? You're usually **fairly** neat ~~fairly~~.
3 Your children are both really tall~~s~~.
4 My best friend is ~~a~~ very funny. He's always telling jokes.
5 Your parents never smile. They're **really** serious people ~~really~~.
6 Are you OK? You're **fairly** quiet ~~fairly~~ today.

2.4 Reading
READING
A

1

B

1 F (Mona De Luca lives with a younger brother and sister.)
2 T
3 F (Mona's father is named Ralph.)
4 F (Ralph's children say he is serious and never laughs or smiles.)
5 F (Mona's grandmother is 79 years old.)
6 T

C

1 d **2** a **3** c **4** e **5** b

2.5 Listening; Functional Language
LISTENING
A

her brother, her cousin, her parents, her brother's wife

B

1 c **2** e **3** d **4** b **5** a

FUNCTIONAL LANGUAGE
2 please **3** course **4** Could **5** sorry **6** not
7 problem **8** that **9** dollars

2.6 Write an email to a friend
WRITING
A

who they live with, what they study,
who is in their class

B

1 T

2 T

3 F (Next year, we have to choose chemistry or biology.)

4 F (Emma doesn't live near the university. It's about 30 minutes away.)

5 T

6 F (Sophie is one of her classmates.)

7 F (Carlos is Emma's roommate.)

8 T

C

1 and **2** but **3** and **4** or **5** or **6** and **7** but
8 and **9** and

WRITING PRACTICE

B

Model answer

Hi Francesco,

It was good to hear from you. I'm very well, thanks. How are you? Are you still going to college?

I'm now working at an advertising company in the center of the city. I'm really enjoying it. The people I work with are very friendly. My boss is also very helpful and she has taught me a lot of new skills.

I'm still living in the same apartment as before. My roommate can be annoying sometimes – he is so messy. He also watches TV late at night, which keeps me awake. I will look for a new place to live next month. Maybe I can find an apartment closer to the office.

Best wishes,

Gianni

3.1 A typical day
VOCABULARY

A

1 get up **2** leave **3** get **4** have **5** have
6 go **7** take **8** read **9** watch **10** go

B

1 d **2** e **3** a **4** c **5** b

GRAMMAR

A

1 live **2** watches **3** listen **4** works **5** has **6** go

B

1 lives **2** get up **3** have **4** works **5** likes
6 teaches **7** go **8** writes

PRONUNCIATION

A

/s/	/z/	/ɪz/
starts	goes	teaches
writes	has	watches
	lives	

B

2 takes **3** works **4** watches **5** writes

3.2 All day, every day
GRAMMAR

A

1 I usually sleep for eight hours a night.

2 Milos and Ali / Ali and Milos are always late for class.

3 Samantha always has three cups of coffee in the morning.

4 My brother sometimes plays soccer on the weekend.

5 It is never really cold in Thailand.

6 I often play video games in the evening.

B

2 Emily never takes a shower in the morning.

3 Emily rarely plays video games on the weekend.

4 Emily always goes to yoga classes.

5 Ben always listens to music on the way to work.

6 Ben usually takes a shower in the morning.

7 Ben sometimes plays video games on the weekend.

8 Ben rarely goes to yoga classes.

PRONUNCIATION

●○○	○●○	●○○	○●○
coffee	Japan	exercise	director
weekend		interesting	umbrella
yoga		radio	

VOCABULARY

A

1 in **2** on **3** on **4** at **5** On **6** in

B

1 My boss usually has meetings **in** the afternoon.

2 I never use my phone **at** night.

3 correct

4 Georgina sometimes goes for a run **on** Saturdays.

5 correct

6 correct

3.3 A special day
GRAMMAR

A

1 don't live **2** don't see **3** doesn't come **4** doesn't enjoy
5 doesn't like **6** doesn't make **7** don't eat

B

1 correct

2 My father **doesn't** ~~don't~~ like science fiction movies.

3 She **doesn't** ~~no~~ listen to music at work.

4 correct

5 I **don't** ~~not~~ speak Spanish very well.

VOCABULARY

Down

2 fireworks **4** party

Across

3 special **5** parades **6** presents **7** decorations

ANSWER KEY 83

Answer key

PRONUNCIATION

1 We <u>always</u> have a <u>party</u> on the <u>4th</u> of <u>July</u>.
2 They <u>don't</u> put up <u>decorations</u> until <u>December</u>.
3 We <u>open</u> our <u>presents</u> in the <u>morning</u>.
4 There's a <u>big</u> <u>parade</u> in <u>November</u>.
5 My <u>mother</u> <u>always</u> <u>makes</u> <u>traditional</u> <u>food</u>.
6 <u>Brad</u> <u>doesn't</u> <u>celebrate</u> his <u>birthday</u>.

3.4 Reading

A
1

B
2 wash up   3 have breakfast   4 call mission control
5 have lunch   6 repair equipment   7 exercise

C
1 T
2 F (After getting up, he always washes up. There isn't
a shower.)
3 T
4 F (In the past, food came out of tubes, but now they eat
a lot of the same food they did on Earth.)
5 F (He says it's 'boring'.)
6 F (Astronauts usually exercise for two hours a day.)
7 T

3.5 Listening; Functional Language

LISTENING

A
have a party, go out to eat, watch a movie

B
1 Saturday   2 twenty-six / 26   3 special   4 big groups
5 money   6 Friday evening   7 seven fifteen / 7:15
8 book the tickets

FUNCTIONAL LANGUAGE

A
1 Why   2 How   3 about   4 Let's
a Awesome   b sure   c sounds   d great

B
1 b   2 d   3 c   4 a

3.6 Write a blog post about your day

WRITING

A
1

B
1 c   2 b   3 c   4 c   5 c   6 b   7 b

C
Before, After that, After breakfast, Then, Finally

D
1 get up
2 have a cup of coffee
3 take a shower
4 get dressed
5 check schedule
6 have breakfast
7 go to the gym
8 have lunch
9 take a nap
10 read a book

WRITING PRACTICE

B
Model answer
During the week, I wake up early every morning. I usually have
coffee and some toast for breakfast. I sometimes listen to the radio
as I get ready for work. I take a shower, get dressed and then drive
to my office.
I'm often very busy at work, so when the office closes, I like to go
for a swim to relax. There is a pool nearby. Then, I go home and
have dinner with my husband. In the evening, I like to read a book
or watch a little TV.
My routine on the weekend is very different. I get up late and visit
friends or family. It's much more fun than going to work!

4.1 What do you do?

VOCABULARY

A
1 businesswoman   2 mechanic   3 dentist   4 engineer
5 hairdresser   6 teacher   7 journalist   8 nurse

B
1 office   2 home   3 travels   4 meetings   5 meet
6 wear   7 computer

C
a journalist   b businesswoman   c teacher   d nurse

GRAMMAR

A
1 c or e   2 e or c   3 d   4 f   5 a   6 b

B
1 Does / doesn't   2 Do / do   3 Does / does   4 Do / don't

C
2 Does your sister work full time?
3 Do you wear a uniform at work?
4 Does your wife travel a lot for work?
5 Does your company have an office in New York?

PRONUNCIATION

2 Does she
3 Do you
4 Does he
5 Does she
6 Do you

84   ANSWER KEY

Answer key

4.2 Good job!
GRAMMAR

A

2 have to wear   **3** doesn't have to work   **4** don't have to pay
5 doesn't have to get up   **6** has to travel

B

2 Do you have to do a lot of training?
3 Do you have to work inside?
4 Do you have to pay for tea and coffee?
5 Do you have to work nine to five?

PRONUNCIATION

1 answer   **2** work   **3** use   **4** start   **5** go   **6** organize

VOCABULARY

A

1 d   **2** a   **3** e   **4** b   **5** c

B

1 early in the morning   **2** noon   **3** nine to five
4 midnight   **5** late in the afternoon

4.3 Learn something new
GRAMMAR

A

1 Where   **2** What   **3** When   **4** why   **5** who   **6** How long
7 How much

B

2 What do you do?
3 Why do you study English?
4 How long does it take to become a teacher?
5 How much does it cost?

PRONUNCIATION

1 <u>Where</u> do you <u>study</u>?
2 <u>What</u> do you <u>study</u>?
3 <u>How long</u> is your <u>course</u>?
4 <u>Who</u> is your <u>teacher</u>?
5 <u>How much</u> do you <u>spend</u> on <u>books</u>?
6 <u>Why</u> do you <u>want</u> to <u>get</u> a <u>degree</u>?

VOCABULARY

A

1 go   **2** study   **3** take   **4** get   **5** train

B

2 a degree   **3** a business   **4** an exam
5 a subject   **6** a qualification

4.4 Reading
READING

A

2

B

1 a   **2** c   **3** b   **4** a   **5** c

C

1 role   **2** 2,000 miles   **3** $35,000   **4** round-trip flights
5 a uniform   **6** contact

4.5 Listening; Functional Language
LISTENING

A

his current job, his work hours, the job he would like, the size of his company

B

1 F (He doesn't work as an actor on TV. / He works as a receptionist.)
2 F (He works in an office.)
3 T
4 T
5 F (He has an hour for lunch at noon.)
6 F (The company is very big.)
7 F (He doesn't think his job is very interesting.)
8 T

FUNCTIONAL LANGUAGE

R = Receptionist   RK = Richard Kershaw

1 **R:**   Good morning. This is Schmidt and Brandt. Can I help you?
2 **RK:** Hello. Could I speak to Hannah Schmidt, please?
3 **R:**   Who's speaking, please?
4 **RK:** It's Richard Kershaw.
5 **R:**   Hold on a minute, please.
6 **R:**   I'm afraid she isn't available right now. Would you like to leave a message?
7 **RK:** Yes, please. Can you ask her to call Richard from S-REK Ltd at 800-555-0199, please?
8 **R:**   I'm sorry, can you repeat that?

4.6 Write an email asking for information
WRITING

A

1 learn   **2** skills   **3** four   **4** morning   **5** contact

B

time of classes, how much the classes cost,
what languages they teach

C

Dear Ms. Souza,
I am writing to ask about your language classes. First, what languages do you offer? Do you have French classes? Second, when are your classes? I am free in the evenings and on the weekend. Do you have classes on Saturdays and Sundays? Finally, how much does the course cost?
I look forward to hearing from you.
All the best,
Pieter Hines

D

1 Greeting and the name of the person you are writing to
2 Reason for writing
3 Asking about the language courses on offer
4 Asking about the times of classes on offer
5 Asking about the cost of the courses
6 Standard 'end of letter' phrase

ANSWER KEY   85

Answer key

WRITING PRACTICE

C
Model answer
Dear Ms. Nagy,
I am writing to ask about your two-day professional interview course. First, how much does the course cost? Second, when is the course? Is it during the week or on the weekend? Finally, where is the course held?
I look forward to hearing from you.
Kind regards,
Alex

5.1 There's no place like home

VOCABULARY

A
1 armchair   2 bathtub   3 fridge   4 shower   5 bed   6 lamp
7 oven   8 toilet   9 dishwasher   10 couch

B

Bedroom	Bathroom	Kitchen	Living room
bed	bathtub	dishwasher	armchair
lamp	shower	fridge	couch
	toilet	lamp	lamp
		oven	

PRONUNCIATION
1 dad   2 blue   3 dig   4 gate   5 boat   6 got

GRAMMAR

A
1 is   2 isn't   3 aren't   4 Is   5 are   6 some   7 any   8 any
9 is   10 are

B
1 There are   2 there is   3 There isn't   4 there are
5 There is   6 there are   7 There aren't

5.2 My neighborhood

VOCABULARY

A
2 park   3 movie theater   4 library   5 subway station
6 supermarket   7 gym   8 museum

B
1 market   2 airport   3 hospital   4 restaurant   5 theater
6 stores

GRAMMAR

A
1 Lizzie can speak Spanish.
2 He can't ride a bike.
3 She can't sing.
4 He can't swim.
5 He can make sushi.
6 Sarah can play the violin.

B
1 We ~~go~~ can't **go** to the movie theater tonight because it's closed.
2 correct
3 David can ~~to~~ speak three languages, English, French and Korean. His mom is French and his dad is South Korean.
4 correct
5 She lives close to her office so she can walk~~s~~ to work in the morning.
6 I play the guitar and I'm in a band. **Can** ~~Do~~ you ~~can~~ play a musical instrument?

PRONUNCIATION
1 weak   2 strong   3 weak   4 strong   5 weak
6 strong   7 weak   8 strong

5.3 Amazing buildings

GRAMMAR

A
1 b
2 e
3 d
4 c
5 a

B
1 Turn   2 Listen   3 push   4 go   5 take   6 Buy   7 touch
8 be

VOCABULARY
1 modern   2 terrible   3 ugly   4 amazing   5 beautiful
6 strange

PRONUNCIATION
2 beautiful   3 amazing   4 ugly   5 interesting   6 strange

5.4 Reading

READING

A
b

B
1 d   2 b   3 d   4 a and d   5 c   6 a and d   7 b   8 b and c

C
1 $2,100   2 gym   3 washing machine   4 bus   5 lock
6 bills   7 subway station   8 on-street

5.5 Listening; Functional Language

LISTENING

A
places to eat, street art, tourism, markets, transportation in the city, parks and green spaces

B

1 T
2 F (Hannah says there are a few amazing restaurants and some really good cafés.)
3 T
4 F (Victor lives in Montreal.)
5 T
6 F (Victor says there is lots of street art.)
7 F (Victor says there are some beautiful old buildings.)
8 T

FUNCTIONAL LANGUAGE

A
1 c   2 f   3 b   4 a   5 d   6 e

B
V = Victor   H = Hannah

1 **V:** Hi Hannah! I'm at the subway station.
2 **H:** Oh, hey Victor! Do you need directions to my apartment?
3 **V:** Yes, please.
4 **H:** OK. Come out of the subway station. There is a bank across from the entrance.
5 **V:** … across from the subway station.
6 **H:** Cross over the road and turn left. Then take the first turn on the right.
7 **V:** First turn on the right …
8 **H:** Walk past the movie theater. It's on the left.
9 **V:** Movie theater on the right …
10 **H:** No, on the left. Walk to the end of the road. My apartment is on the left next to the café.

5.6 Write a description of a place
WRITING

A
2

B
famous, high, amazing, old, white, beautiful, red, gold, old, long, interesting, pretty, nice, quiet, great

C
2 Where is it?
3 What does it look like?
4 What can you see there? / What can you do there?
5 What is it like?

WRITING PRACTICE

C
Model answer
The Burj Khalifa is currently the tallest skyscraper in the world. It is in Dubai in the United Arab Emirates. There are wonderful views from the top floor. You can see the whole of Dubai, the ocean and the desert outside of the city.

The Burj Khalifa is made from glass, metal and concrete. The building gets narrow closer to the top. It has a total of 163 floors.

In front of the Burj Khalifa is a big, beautiful fountain. Inside there are restaurants, offices, a gym and even a hotel. It is an amazing building.

6.1 Let's go out
VOCABULARY

A
1 festival   2 exhibit   3 comedy show   4 theater
5 concert   6 movie theater

B
1 exhibit   2 theater   3 movie theater   4 festival
5 comedy show   6 concert

PRONUNCIATION
2 Oo
3 Ooo
4 ooOo
5 Oo
6 Oo

GRAMMAR

A
1 I don't like stay**ing** in all the time!
2 I love~~s~~ **going** to the movie theater.
3 They love~~s~~ ~~to~~ playing soccer.
4 He ~~not~~ **doesn't** like watch**ing** TV.
5 I hate~~s~~ pizza!
6 We ~~not~~ **don't** like visit**ing** museums.

B
1 Ahmad loves going to festivals.
2 He likes eating Italian food.
3 He doesn't like playing video games.
4 He hates going to the theater.
5 He hates listening to pop music.

6.2 It was fun
GRAMMAR

A
1 Where were your parents born?
2 My train was really busy this morning.
3 I was in Tokyo for business last month.
4 The tickets were really expensive!
5 How was the concert last night?
6 That was a really terrible movie!
7 It was really hot all last week.

B
2 were   3 wasn't   4 was   5 weren't   6 was   7 was
8 wasn't   9 were   10 was   11 were   12 wasn't

PRONUNCIATION
1 /wʌz/
2 /wəz/
3 /wər/
4 /wɜːr/
5 /wər/
6 /wɜːr/
7 /wʌz/
8 /wʌz/

Answer key

VOCABULARY

A

1 in **2** in **3** ago **4** Last **5** in **6** ago

B

1 The first Oscar ceremony was ~~last~~ **in** 1929.
2 They were at the movie theater ~~in~~ **last** night.
3 correct
4 correct
5 Peter was at college five years ~~last~~ **ago**.
6 correct

6.3 Life stories
GRAMMAR

A

1 was	**6** worked
2 started / began	**7** made
3 reached	**8** won
4 moved	**9** died
5 began / started	**10** released

B

1 took **2** went **3** moved **4** bought **5** saw **6** started
7 met **8** won

PRONUNCIATION

1 /ɪd/	**5** /d/
2 /t/	**6** /d/
3 /t/	**7** /t/
4 /d/	**8** /ɪd/

VOCABULARY

1 went **2** studied **3** started **4** became **5** got **6** moved
7 was **8** had

6.4 Reading
READING

A

1 *Laugh Night* **2** *The Blade* **3** *3200*

B

1 T
2 F (The writer recommends *3200*.)
3 T
4 F (The writer didn't think *Laugh Night* was funny.)
5 F (The writer wasn't surprised that *The Blade* was so good.)
6 T

C

1 Emma Davies
2 Damian Shultz (and) Greta Simons
3 Ivan Rodriguez
4 Tosh Ellis

6.5 Listening; Functional Language
LISTENING

A

1 The actors **2** The special effects **3** The music
4 The director

B

1 a **2** b **3** a **4** b **5** c **6** c

FUNCTIONAL LANGUAGE

2 loved **3** awful **4** about **5** sure
6 awesome **7** think **8** OK **9** hate

6.6 Write a review of an event
WRITING

B

People throw tomatoes at each other.

C

1 F (Laura went to the festival with three of her friends.)
2 F (The ticket cost $175, which included three nights at the hotel.)
3 F (They stayed in a hotel in Valencia.)
4 T
5 F (The whole event lasted an hour.)
6 T

D

1 c **2** e **3** a **4** b **5** d

E

first, next, then, after that, finally

F

1 First, we waited in the line to get into the venue.
2 Next, actors dressed in 1920s costumes showed us to our seats.
3 Then, we watched the first half of the movie.
4 After that, we had dinner while a live band played music from the movie.
5 Finally, we watched the end of the movie. It was a great night.

WRITING PRACTICE

B

Model answer

Last year I went to the Edinburgh Festival Fringe in Scotland for the first time. It is the largest arts festival in the world. I went there with my friend Maria.

We stayed in a guesthouse near the city center. It was fairly expensive as thousands of people come to Edinburgh for the festival. There are lots of different shows to go and see, but it is mostly famous for its comedy shows. Some of the shows are free and some cost around $60.

The venues are all over the city so you should plan your day carefully. The festival goes on for 25 days in August.

After the festival ends, prizes are awarded to the performers, for example best show, best joke, etc. It was a great experience and I'd love to go again.

Answer key

7.1 Getting around
VOCABULARY
A
1 subway train 2 taxi 3 ferry 4 plane 5 trolley
6 bicycle

B
1 boat 2 plane 3 bicycle 4 trolley 5 bus 6 motorcycle

PRONUNCIATION

/eɪ/	/oʊ/
main	boat
plane	coach
same	motorcycle
train	phone

GRAMMAR
1 could 2 couldn't 3 couldn't 4 could 5 could
6 couldn't

7.2 A love of adventure
VOCABULARY
A
1 travel 2 the flight 3 the scooter 4 the hotel
5 the motorcycle

B
1 returned from New York
2 take a taxi
3 arrived at the hotel
4 missed the bus
5 left the station

GRAMMAR
2 Mae didn't study German at school.
3 I didn't see Simon and Alison at the party on Saturday.
4 I didn't go to the gym after work.
5 I didn't like math when I was in school.
6 Lizzie didn't finish the report yesterday.
7 I didn't speak to him after the meeting.
8 Molly didn't enjoy that movie last night.

PRONUNCIATION
2 Bang**kok** 3 Ber**lin** 4 Ca**ra**cas 5 Mi**lan** 6 Kathman**du**
7 **Lis**bon 8 Ma**ni**la 9 **Mum**bai 10 Chi**ca**go

7.3 A trip to remember
GRAMMAR
2 Did you go 3 where did you have 4 what did you eat
5 was 6 Did you take 7 When did

PRONUNCIATION
1 What did‿you‿do on the weekend?
2 How long did‿you work there?
3 They stayed there for‿two weeks.
4 Susan didn't want‿to‿go home.
5 Did‿you have fun?
6 Where did‿you go last summer?
7 Did‿you stay‿in‿a hotel?
8 We went to‿a lot‿of museums.

VOCABULARY
1 went 2 got 3 met 4 ate 5 took

7.4 Reading
READING
A
1 c 2 a 3 b

B
1 a 2 b 3 b 4 a 5 a 6 a 7 b 8 a

C
1 farm worker 2 hostel worker 3 tour guide 4 tour guide
5 hostel worker 6 farm worker 7 farm worker

7.5 Listening; Functional Language
LISTENING
A

B
1 T
2 F (He traveled from Paris to Athens by bus.)
3 F (He bought a motorcycle in Mumbai.)
4 T
5 F (He says he met a lot of amazing people.)
6 T

FUNCTIONAL LANGUAGE
1 afternoon 2 reservation 3 passport 4 checkout
5 included 6 help 7 wi-fi 8 password

7.6 Write a short article about a travel experience
WRITING
A
1 c 2 a 3 e 4 d

B
1 December or Cambodia 2 expensive hotel
3 souvenirs 4 too hot 5 tourists

C
1 because 2 so 3 because 4 because 5 so

Answer key

WRITING PRACTICE

B
Model answer
A few years ago, I went to Shanghai in China with my two friends.
We all love modern cities, so we were excited to go.
Shanghai is a huge city with lots of restaurants, stores and hotels.
We stayed at a hotel in Jing'an – an area of the city famous for
its large temple. It wasn't too expensive and the rooms were
very clean.
There are two sides of the city to visit – Puxi, which is more
historical, and Pudong, which is famous for its skyscrapers. We did
a lot of sightseeing and shopping in both sides of the city!
For me it was a wonderful trip because it was so different from
where I am from. Also the food was delicious. I would definitely
recommend going.

8.1 I'm hungry!
VOCABULARY

A
Down
2 rice **5** fish **7** milk **8** orange
Across
3 yogurt **4** coffee **6** tomato **9** banana **10** juice

GRAMMAR

A

This week, I'm trying to be healthier. So instead of snacks like
a bar of chocolate, I'll eat ~~any~~ some fruit, like ~~a~~ an apple, a banana
or some oranges. I never eat breakfast, but this morning, I had a
bowl of cereal with milk~~s~~ and ~~a~~ toast without ~~some~~ any butter.
At lunchtime, I went to a café near where I work. I ordered some
brown rice~~s~~ with chicken and a glass of juice~~s~~. Then for dessert I
had some yogurt.
In the evening, I usually have some sandwiches, but this evening,
I'm going to have some fish~~es~~ with ~~a~~ vegetables and ~~any~~ some
cheese~~s~~ and biscuits.

B

Countable singular	Countable plural	Uncountable
apple	chips	pasta
banana	hamburgers	rice
cookie	potatoes	toast
mushroom	sandwiches	yogurt

PRONUNCIATION

1 chips **2** tomatoes **3** peas

8.2 What we eat
VOCABULARY

1 rice **2** sparkling water **3** yogurt **4** chocolates **5** sauce
6 yogurt

PRONUNCIATION

Short vowel sounds: apple, bread, chicken, eggs, cup
Long vowel sounds: beans, cheese, food, fruit, tea

GRAMMAR

A
1 much **2** a lot of **3** many **4** a lot of **5** much
6 a lot of **7** a lot of **8** many **9** much **10** much

B
1 How ~~many~~ much bread do you usually eat?
2 correct
3 Karen drinks ~~much~~ a lot of coffee in the morning.
4 correct
5 There aren't ~~much~~ many bananas left. Can you buy some?
6 How ~~much~~ many people did you invite to the party?

8.3 Yes, chef!
GRAMMAR

A
1 a or an **2** the **3** no article **4** the **5** no article

B
1 – **2** an **3** – **4** the **5** – **6** the **7** an **8** an **9** a
10 the **11** the **12** The **13** a **14** the

PRONUNCIATION

1 flour **2** fruit **3** healthy **4** bottle **5** vegetables
6 fry **7** bowl **8** sandwich

VOCABULARY

A
1 Put **2** Crack **3** Beat **4** Heat **5** fry **6** Serve

B
1 peel **2** grate **3** Put **4** serve **5** fry **6** chop **7** Add

8.4 Reading
READING

A
2 Unusual food

B
1 c **2** a **3** b **4** c **5** b

C
1 adjective **2** noun **3** verb **4** adjective **5** noun

D
1 c **2** d **3** a **4** e **5** b

8.5 Listening; Functional Language
LISTENING

A
1 Oli **2** Tara **3** Tara

B
1 c **2** b **3** b **4** b **5** a **6** c

FUNCTIONAL LANGUAGE

A
1 f **2** d **3** b **4** a **5** c **6** e

Answer key

8.6 Write an online restaurant review
WRITING

A
2 one of the cats
3 the waitress
4 the chocolate cake and tea with milk
5 the café

B
1 it 2 It 3 It 4 she 5 they 6 them 7 she 8 him

C
1 His girlfriend
2 The restaurant was dark. / They couldn't see the menu.
3 Pasta
4 Delicious
5 It was cold.

WRITING PRACTICE

B

Model answer
Carlo's ★ ★ ★ ★ ☆
I love Italian food, so I was really pleased when this restaurant opened in the city center. I went there for my birthday last month with a group of friends and family. The restaurant has huge wood-burning ovens and you can see the chefs making the pizza. There are over 30 different types of pizza to choose from. The waiter was from Naples and was very helpful. He told us which pizzas were his favorite so we ordered those!

9.1 People watching
VOCABULARY
1 cap, jeans, sneakers
2 skirt, scarf, coat, boots, socks
3 boots, jeans, sweater
4 sunglasses, jeans

PRONUNCIATION
1 sk<u>ir</u>t 2 pref<u>er</u> 3 n<u>ur</u>se 4 <u>ear</u>n 5 w<u>or</u>k 6 g<u>ir</u>l
7 p<u>er</u>son 8 l<u>ear</u>n

GRAMMAR

A
2 'm looking 3 you're shopping 4 Sara is helping
5 Are we / having 6 I'm / We're leaving 7 Is Ben coming
8 is he working 9 he isn't working

B
1 Is he riding a bike? 2 Is he eating pizza?
3 Is she playing the piano? 4 Are they running in the park?

C
1 Yes, he is. 2 Yes, he is. 3 Yes, she is. 4 No, they aren't.

9.2 Job swap
VOCABULARY

A
1 These days 2 at the moment 3 today 4 right now
5 now 6 currently

B
1 currently 2 right now 3 today 4 now 5 these days
6 At the moment

GRAMMAR

A
1 work 2 isn't helping 3 are they watching 4 ride
5 walks 6 are you leaving 7 aren't closing

B
1 You should wear a scarf – **it's snowing** outside.
2 We ~~aren't~~ **don't** usually play~~ing~~ tennis every day.
3 correct
4 **Do** ~~Are~~ you usually go~~ing~~ to the beach?
5 correct
6 She isn't currently cook**ing** in the kitchen.
7 Are they walk**ing** to school?

PRONUNCIATION
1 sung 2 walking 4 pink 5 younger 8 strong

9.3 Shop till you drop
GRAMMAR

A

Subject pronoun	Object pronoun
I	me
he	him
she	her
it	it
we	us
you	you
they	them

B
1 us 2 it 3 them 4 it 5 him 6 her 7 you

VOCABULARY

A
1 dentist's 2 pharmacy 3 bank 4 department store
5 hairdresser's

B
2 bakery 3 butcher's 4 market 5 bookstore 6 library
7 newsstand 8 department store

PRONUNCIATION
1 /tʃ/ 2 /ʃ/ 3 /ʃ/ 4 /tʃ/ 5 /ʃ/ 6 /ʃ/ 7 /tʃ/ 8 /ʃ/

ANSWER KEY 91

Answer key

9.4 Reading
READING

A

1 b **2** a

B

1 be easy **2** for a walk **3** much fun **4** really sleep
5 to walk everywhere **6** enough time **7** in the end

C

1 damage **2** organizing **3** uploading **4** crazy
5 under pressure **6** terrible

9.5 Listening; Functional Language
LISTENING

A

b 5 **c** 4 **d** 3 **e** 2

B

1 T
2 F (Max Out has lots of bargains.)
3 T
4 F (They sell high-quality products at low prices.)
5 T
6 F (You can buy ties, scarves, gloves and sunglasses at TieUp.)

FUNCTIONAL LANGUAGE

1 Can I help you **2** I'm just looking **3** can I try
4 the changing rooms **5** look really great **6** a little small
7 in medium **8** How much are they **9** I'll take them

9.6 Write a social media post
WRITING

A

2

B

1 Mae **2** Hannah **3** Luke **4** Hannah **5** Luke **6** Hannah

C

1 We're **going** for our usual walk through the woods.
2 You have to be careful as some are ~~in danger~~ **dangerous,** but there are lots that are delicious.
3 We're having a ~~grate~~ **great** time and trying to see how high we can get.
4 ~~I am~~ **I'm/I am** happy we're inside~~.~~, as ~~As~~ we don't have to worry about the weather.
5 We're traveling down to London to watch a play~~?~~.
6 ~~m~~**M**om packed some sandwiches for us~~.~~: so we're all eating those.

WRITING PRACTICE

B

Model answer

We're at the beach for the first time this year. We're all so happy! Sophie's going to go for a swim; Juan and Luca are playing volleyball. As for me, I'm relaxing and sunbathing for the rest of the day! Tom.

10.1 The right location
VOCABULARY

A

1 lake **2** island **3** forest **4** mountains **5** beaches
6 ocean **7** hills **8** jungle **9** river **10** desert

GRAMMAR

A

2 older
3 easier
4 more famous
5 better
6 cheaper
7 closer
8 more expensive
9 dirtier
10 worse
11 more comfortable
12 stranger

B

2 I find science harder / more difficult than geography.
3 The swimming pool was hotter / warmer than the ocean.
4 My house is bigger / larger than Juan's apartment.
5 The weather in the summer is sunnier than in the spring.
6 Her first novel was better than her second.

PRONUNCIATION

1 bigger than **2** busier than **3** higher than
4 younger than **5** longer than **6** expensive than

10.2 Where on Earth?
VOCABULARY

1 Spring
2 sunny
3 windy
4 Summer
5 hot
6 rains
7 Fall
8 foggy
9 winter
10 snows
11 cold

92 ANSWER KEY

Answer key

PRONUNCIATION
1 /aʊ/ 2 /oʊ/ 3 /aʊ/ 4 /oʊ/
5 /oʊ/ 6 /aʊ/ 7 /aʊ/ 8 /oʊ/

GRAMMAR

A

Adjective	Comparative	Superlative
tall	taller	tallest
dry	drier	driest
hot	hotter	hottest
kind	kinder	kindest
busy	busier	busiest
bad	worse	worst
crowded	more crowded	most crowded
ancient	more ancient	most ancient
good	better	best

B
2 The Volga is the longest river in Europe.
3 La Paz in Bolivia is the highest capital city in the world.
4 The mosquito is the most dangerous insect in the world.
5 Finland is the happiest country in the world.
6 What is the fastest car in the world?
7 What is the wettest season?
8 Who is your best friend?
9 What is the most expensive city in Europe?
10 Who is the friendliest person you know?

10.3 Survival
VOCABULARY
1 set off 2 Find out 3 look for 4 take off 5 put on
6 give up

GRAMMAR

A
1 They hope to get married in June.
2 He wanted to know more about history.
3 Don't forget to email Hannah.
4 Thanks for helping me to find my keys.
5 Sam is trying to work harder at college.

B
1 David never remembers **to lock** ~~locking~~ the door – I'm surprised we haven't been robbed!
2 What have you decided **to do** ~~doing~~?
3 correct
4 David plans **to** visit~~ing~~ his cousin in Canada next year.
5 She learned **to** read~~ing~~ when she was five years old.
6 correct

PRONUNCIATION
1 /tə/ 2 /tuː/ 3 /tə/ 4 /tə/ 5 /tuː/ 6 /tuː/

10.4 Reading
READING

C
1 b 2 c 3 a 4 c

D
1 O 2 F 3 F 4 O 5 F 6 O 7 F

10.5 Listening; Functional Language
LISTENING

A
2

B
b, c, d

C
1 adventure 2 true story 3 remote part 4 the weather
5 broke his leg 6 accident 7 their camp 8 three days

FUNCTIONAL LANGUAGE
1 I'm away 2 free on 3 I'd love to 4 having 5 come
6 sounds 7 to come 8 would be great

10.6 Write a product review
WRITING

A
1 a camping stove 2 a backpack 3 a pair of walking boots
4 a first aid kit

B
a 3 b 1 c 2

C
2 easily 3 carefully 4 well 5 quickly

D

	Review a	Review b	Review c
What is the product?	A pair of walking boots	A camping stove	A backpack
What are its bad points?	They are difficult to put on and don't keep his feet dry	It can only really boil water	-
What are its good points?	-	It's good for boiling water	It's big and light It has lots of special parts
Would the reviewer recommend it?	No	No	Yes

ANSWER KEY 93

Answer key

WRITING PRACTICE

B

Model answer

I bought these gloves for my annual ski trip. They are made with a special material so you can grip the ski poles more easily. Unfortunately, they don't keep out the cold at all. I ended up having to buy a warmer pair at the ski resort.

11.1 Health tips

VOCABULARY

1 leg   **2** foot   **3** heart   **4** neck   **5** arm   **6** nose   **7** eye
8 brain   **9** hand   **10** ear

GRAMMAR

A

1 **Should we** We should go to the beach today or tomorrow?
2 A: I should buy John a birthday present.
   B: No, you should**n't**. He didn't buy you one.
3 We're going on vacation in August so the weather should **be** sunny.
4 They shouldn't to talk to their mom like that.

B

2 You shouldn't eat nuts.
3 You should study now.
4 You should relax more.
5 You should walk sometimes.

PRONUNCIATION

1 You should try to eat lots of fruits and vegetables.
2 You shouldn't drink too much tea.
3 You should get plenty of exercise.
4 You shouldn't worry about it too much.
5 You should exercise your brain every day.

11.2 In it to win it

GRAMMAR

A

2 Have you ever ridden an elephant?
3 I've never been to Japan. / I haven't been to Japan.
4 She's written ten books.
5 I've never lived abroad. / I haven't lived abroad.
6 Have you ever run a marathon?

B

2 Roberto hasn't bought a house.
3 Lucy hasn't climbed Kilimanjaro.
4 Roberto has been to New York.
5 They have (both) eaten octopus.
6 Lucy has flown a plane.
7 Roberto hasn't taken a photo on the Great Wall of China.
8 They haven't won the lottery.

VOCABULARY

1 b   **2** c   **3** b   **4** a   **5** b   **6** c   **7** a   **8** c

PRONUNCIATION

1 forgotten   **2** won   **3** gone   **4** seen   **5** won

11.3 Move it

GRAMMAR

A

1 I played   **2** he joined   **3** We went   **4** 've never been
5 rained   **6** 've done

B

1 went   **2** has climbed / 's climbed   **3** have read / 've read
4 saw   **5** got married   **6** haven't seen

PRONUNCIATION

1 b
2 a
3 b
4 b
5 a

VOCABULARY

1 play golf
2 play badminton
3 go swimming
4 do gymnastics
5 play tennis
6 do yoga
7 play basketball
8 go surfing
9 do karate
10 go ice-skating

11.4 Reading

READING

B
2

C

1 F (He started ten years ago.)
2 F (His doctor told him to do more exercise.)
3 T
4 T
5 T

D

1 The doctor told Martin to do more exercise.
2 Martin joined a local club.
3 Martin learned to climb on an indoor wall.
4 Martin did his first outdoor club.
5 Martin broke a bone in his foot.

Answer key

11.5 Listening; Functional Language

LISTENING

A
boxing, running, swimming, yoga

B
1 Sophie   2 Hannah   3 Hannah   4 Sophie
5 Sophie   6 Sophie

FUNCTIONAL LANGUAGE

A
1 When
2 how long
3 How much
4 Do I
5 Are there
6 Can I

11.6 Write a recommendation on a forum

WRITING

A
Losing weight

C
1 Not to worry about his weight
2 Swimming
3 Walk or bike everywhere, try to eat healthy food and not so much chocolate

D
1 too / as well   2 also   3 too / as well

WRITING PRACTICE

B
Model answer
Hi Larry, why don't you try watching aerobic videos online? There are some really good ones for people who are starting to exercise more. It also means you can exercise at home. You could try eating more fruit as well.

12.1 Life's too busy

GRAMMAR

A
2 I'm going to go to the movie theater with my friends.
3 Tim isn't going to finish his essay.
4 How are you going to get home?
5 Emma is going to start college in September.
6 My mother isn't going to cook tonight.
7 What are you going to have for lunch?
8 Darren is going to run a marathon this weekend.

B
1 going to   2 not going to   3 going to   4 going to
5 not going to   6 going to   7 not going to   8 going to

PRONUNCIATION
1 /tə/   2 /tuː/   3 /tə/   4 /tuː/   5 /tə/

VOCABULARY
1 Do you know what time we're going to arrive ~~next~~ tomorrow?
2 Simon's going to travel to New York on **the** weekend.
3 I'm going to call Giovanni and ask him to ~~soon~~ come over **soon**.
4 Are you going to study at the university **next** year ~~next~~?
5 Megan is going to get married this ~~one~~ summer.
6 They're not going to arrive here until later ~~this~~ tonight.

12.2 Everything will be shiny

GRAMMAR
1 will   2 will   3 will   4 won't   5 will   6 won't   7 will
8 will   9 won't   10 will

VOCABULARY
1 get a coffee   2 get some cash   3 got a new job
4 get any sugar   5 get some new clothes   6 getting married
7 get home

PRONUNCIATION
1 b   2 a   3 a   4 b   5 b

12.3 Communication

VOCABULARY
1 blog   2 share   3 uploaded   4 follow   5 likes
6 connected   7 chat   8 tweet

PRONUNCIATION

A
2 f
3 g
4 c
5 b
6 a
7 d

B
1 chat   2 tourist   3 blog   4 know

GRAMMAR

A
1 might be   2 might take   3 might not stay   4 might leave
5 might not join   6 might go   7 might see

B
1 a   2 b   3 b   4 a

12.4 Reading

READING

C
cell phones, power, battery, robots

D
1 c   2 b   3 a   4 b   5 c

ANSWER KEY   95

Answer key

12.5 Listening; Functional Language

LISTENING

B
1 b
2 a
3 c

C
1 F (He thinks there will be flying cars.)
2 T
3 F (When Jenny was young there were no cell phones.)
4 T
5 F (Richard doesn't think life will be the same as it is now.)
6 F (Ellen hates the idea of not eating fresh food.)

FUNCTIONAL LANGUAGE
1 Don't worry
2 It doesn't matter
3 I love it
4 That's terrible
5 That's a shame
6 No problem

12.6 Write a formal email

WRITING

A
c

B
1 Dear Ms. Stevenson,
2 I am writing to you to inform you that we plan to attend Liam's graduation party on June 2nd.
3 We will fly over from France on June 1st, so we will need to stay at a hotel in York.
4 Can you let us know if there are any rooms at The Baytree, or can you suggest a suitable hotel?
5 Also, we will rent a car at the airport. Is there a parking lot at The Baytree where we can leave the car?
6 We look forward to hearing from you.
7 Kind regards, Pierre (and Mari) Lefevre

C
1 To say they will be coming and to ask for some information
2 France
3 June 1st
4 By car
5 If there are any rooms available and if there is a parking lot

WRITING PRACTICE

A
A 21st birthday party

C
Model answer
Dear Sir/Madam,
I am writing to confirm I will be attending Amy's 21st birthday party on March 28th.
Can you please provide me with the address of the venue.
Also, what time does the party start and what time is it expected to end?
I look forward to hearing from you.
Kind regards,
Emma Sanchez